Structure
of Algebra

by

VINCENT H. HAAG

Professor of Mathematics
Franklin and Marshall College

ADDISON-WESLEY PUBLISHING COMPANY

READING, MASSACHUSETTS • PALO ALTO • LONDON • DON MILLS, ONTARIO

This book is in the

**ADDISON-WESLEY SERIES IN SCIENCE AND
MATHEMATICS EDUCATION**

Consulting Editors

RICHARD S. PIETERS   PAUL ROSENBLOOM
GEORGE B. THOMAS, JR.   JOHN WAGNER

Preface

The so-called "new approach" to the teaching of mathematics is no longer an experiment. In this country and abroad there is widespread approval and use of materials that reflect the new thinking about mathematics education.

In all the new thinking there appears to be a common theme: *mathematics must be based on understanding.* In the past, mathematics was too often presented as a set of techniques and rules to be memorized; as soon as a rule was forgotten, the manipulative skill developed with the rule was lost also.

Now the trend is toward the teaching of ideas, and it is felt that skills should evolve out of the ideas. This book deals with the mathematical ideas on which elementary algebra is based. It gives a development of the real number system and its subsystems. In doing this, it describes the structure of a mathematical system, called a complete ordered field. Everything studied in elementary algebra is a consequence of the properties of this system.

This book can be used in a one-term course in mathematics for prospective teachers of algebra, or in an in-service course or summer institute for teachers who are preparing to teach modern materials. Chapters 1 and 2 are short introductions to operations on a set and to the language used in studying mathematical systems. Here we discuss the questions, "What is a proof?" and "Why bother with proofs in school algebra?" In Chapter 3 the idea of an ordered field is introduced, and its properties are developed in some detail. Here the teacher comes to grips with the structure of school algebra. Theorems marked with a star (*) are left to the reader for proof; these are part of the development and should be regarded as strongly recommended exercises.

In Chapter 4 some of the subsystems of the reals are studied, and we see how the familiar properties of integers and rational numbers arise. In Chapter 5 the real numbers are finally characterized as the elements of a complete ordered field. Here we see the subtle distinction between rational and real numbers, the distinction that must be made clear to students on an intuitive level. In the remaining chapters, representations of the real numbers are given, the reals are extended to the complex number system, and the relations and operations of algebra are unified through the concept of function.

III

This volume is based on, and is an expansion of, a preliminary version (*Structure of Elementary Algebra*, copyright by Yale University) written by the author with the support of the School Mathematics Study Group. Acknowledgment is hereby made for permission to reprint in this volume portions of the preliminary version. However, this permission must not be construed as an endorsement by the School Mathematics Study Group of the present volume. The author is indebted to a committee consisting of C. W. Curtis, B. J. Pettis, H. O. Pollak, and C. E. Rickart, who supervised the writing of the *Study*, and to E. A. Cameron, whose comments were helpful in preparing the revision. The author's hope, which is shared by every group interested in new mathematics materials, is that teachers will bring to their classrooms new and clearer views of the mathematics they are teaching.

Lancaster, Pa.   V.H.H.
September 1963

Contents

Chapter 1

Mathematical Systems

1-1. INTRODUCTION

In recent years the teacher of elementary algebra has been challenged to "modernize" his courses. Modernization has various meanings for various people. To some it means a change to more concise terminology. To others it means a deductive approach to the subject. To still others it means an incorporation of the attitudes of present-day mathematics. To many it means some combination of these.

The new textbooks in algebra are beginning to reflect this trend toward modernization. As the new materials find wider adoption in the schools, each teacher (as well as prospective teacher) is faced with the problem of evaluating the various programs and finding the materials that he thinks will best fit the needs of his classes. To do this, he must know what he is looking for. He must first understand the mathematical basis for the course he is teaching or expects to teach. A set of skills in manipulation of symbols and solution of equations is not enough.

This is the central question to which the book is addressed: what is the structure of elementary algebra and how can an understanding of this structure enhance the teaching of algebra?

To find an answer to this question we should first study the structure of some example of a mathematical system, such as a group. Then we should review the language used in algebra before looking at the structure of the system of real numbers, the system on which elementary algebra is based.

1-2. STRUCTURE OF A MATHEMATICAL SYSTEM

In the preceding paragraph we used several familiar words in a new way when we indicated that a "group" is an example of a "mathematical system" whose "structure" needs to be studied. Before defining these words, let us gain some preparatory experience with the ideas involved.

Consider as an example the set of positive integers

$$\{1, 2, 3, 4, \ldots\}.$$

Note that the word "set" has the usual meaning of collection, class, or aggregate of elements. We usually indicate a set of elements by enclosing the elements in braces, { }. In the listing of the above set of positive integers, the three dots mean "and so forth," or "without end." There are several familiar operations we can define on this set. For example, addition is an operation on the positive integers; with each pair of positive integers, addition associates a number. With 3 and 4, addition associates the number 7; with 5 and 4, addition associates 9, etc. Other ways of saying this are: addition attaches the number 9 to the numbers 5 and 4; or, corresponding to the numbers 5 and 4, there is a number, 9, given by addition.

Multiplication is another familiar operation on the set of positive integers. To each pair of positive integers, multiplication attaches one number. To 3 and 1, multiplication attaches 3; with 4 and 3, multiplication associates 12, etc.

The general meaning of "operation on a set" becomes clearer when we look at an unfamiliar operation. Consider, for example, the set of four integers $\{0, 1, 2, 3\}$. Let us define an operation on this set as follows. Select any element of the set, say 3, and then again select any element, say 2. With this ordered pair of elements let the operation associate exactly one number according to this rule: determine the sum of 3 and 2, divide the sum by 4, and find the remainder. Let this remainder be the number that the operation associates with 3 and 2. Let us indicate this association by writing

$$3 \oplus 2 = 1.$$

(We use "$=$" to mean that the symbols "$3 \oplus 2$" and "1" represent the same element of the set.) Similarly,

$$1 \oplus 2 = 3, \qquad 2 \oplus 2 = 0, \qquad 3 \oplus 1 = 0, \qquad \text{etc.}$$

Here we have defined a binary operation $\oplus$ on ordered pairs of elements of the set $\{0, 1, 2, 3\}$; we say

> a *binary operation* on a set S is a rule whereby to each ordered pair of elements of the set S there corresponds exactly one element of some set T.

For the above example we can show all the results of the operation $\oplus$ in tabular form:

$\oplus$	0	1	2	3
0	0	1	2	3
1	1	2	3	0
2	2	3	0	1
3	3	0	1	2

where the first element is chosen from the left column, the second element from the top row, and the result of the operation is found at the intersection of the corresponding row and column of the table.

If the operation associates with each single element of a set exactly one element, we say that the operation is *unary*. Familiar examples of binary operations are ordinary addition and multiplication; some common unary operations are squaring and doubling.

The above set $\{0, 1, 2, 3\}$ with the operation $\oplus$ is an example of a mathematical system.

> A *mathematical system* consists of a set of elements and one or more operations on the elements.

If we denote the set $\{0, 1, 2, 3\}$ by the letter T, then the above mathematical system may be denoted by $(T, \oplus)$.

Let us examine some of the properties of $(T, \oplus)$. (By *property* we mean a relationship among elements and operations which is true for all the elements.)

(1) The first thing we notice is that every entry in the table is an element of T. More precisely, if a, b are any elements of T, then $a \oplus b$ is an element of T. We say in general that

> a set S is *closed under a binary operation* $*$ if for any elements x, y in S, $x * y$ is an element of S.

(2) We also notice a symmetry in the table. For example, $2 \oplus 3 = 3 \oplus 2$, $1 \oplus 3 = 3 \oplus 1$, etc. This is the result of a property of $\oplus$ that can be described as follows: if a, b are any elements of T, then $a \oplus b = b \oplus a$. We say that an operation having this property is *commutative*.

(3) We see that the binary operation $\oplus$ is also *associative;* that is, for any elements a, b, c in T,

$$a \oplus (b \oplus c) = (a \oplus b) \oplus c.$$

For example,

$$2 \oplus (2 \oplus 3) = (2 \oplus 2) + 3.$$

(4) Among the elements of T we call the element 0 an *identity* element for $\oplus$ because

$$0 \oplus 1 = 1 \oplus 0 = 1, \qquad 0 \oplus 2 = 2 \oplus 0 = 2, \qquad \text{etc.}$$

In general, $0 \oplus a = a \oplus 0 = a$ for any element a in T. That is, any element of T is left unchanged when it is combined with an identity. In general,

an element i of a set S is an *identity* for the operation $*$ if

$$x * i = i * x = x$$

for every x in S.

(5) Inspection of the table shows that each row and each column contain an identity element exactly once. This follows from the fact that each element of T has an *inverse* under $\oplus$: to each element a in T there corresponds an element b in T such that $a \oplus b = b \oplus a = 0$. In general,

if i is an identity for the operation $*$ in a set S, then x and y are *inverses* under $*$ if

$$x * y = y * x = i.$$

Of course, in a system the elements may be any objects whatsoever and the operations completely arbitrary. Algebra is concerned not with the elements or the symbols for the elements of a system; it is interested in the *structure* of the system as described by the basic properties which its operations possess.

The elements of T are quite specific in our minds: they are the integers 0, 1, 2, 3. The operation $\oplus$ is also specific because it involves the familiar operations of addition and dividing by 4. The resulting system $(T, \oplus)$ therefore has properties which are not surprising to us; in fact, we are led to these properties by our intuitive notions about integers and about addition and dividing by 4. To avoid the prejudices of intuition let us try to forget the meanings of 0, 1, 2, 3 and $\oplus$. Instead, let us write, respectively, s, m, t, r and $*$. Then the table looks like this:

$*$	s	m	t	r
s	s	m	t	r
m	m	t	r	s
t	t	r	s	m
r	r	s	m	t

The resulting system is *abstract* in the sense that the symbols are undefined and the operation $*$ has no meaning other than that given by the table. Let us call this the abstract $(S, *)$-system.

Relieved of our preset ideas about integers, we might be able to discover hidden properties of the $(S, *)$-system that are inherent in the table. Then, since the table for $(T, \oplus)$ has exactly the same form as the table for $(S, *)$, that is, the systems have the same *structure*, what we discover about $(S, *)$ must also be true for $(T, \oplus)$. Thus, through the device of studying the structure of a corresponding abstract system we may discover properties of a familiar system that we never suspected.

We say that the specific system $(T, \oplus)$ is a *model* of the abstract system $(S, *)$. Many other models can be formed merely by giving other specific meanings to s, m, t, r and $*$. Thus, a system may admit many different models, each with the same structure as the system which it is modeling. But two systems are different only if their structures are different.

This connection between systems, models, and structure can be further illustrated by more elementary examples. It is easy to invent an abstract system by choosing any set of elements, writing out a double-entry table, and filling in the cells arbitrarily with elements. Then an operation ∘ is defined from the table by letting $x \circ y$ be the element in row x and column y.

The systems that people construct are usually chosen because some specific models of the system have appeared elsewhere in mathematics, physics, or some other field. As an example, let a set have two elements: a, "the action of reversing an electric switch," and b, "the action of not reversing the switch." If the operation ∘ is defined so that $x \circ y$ is the action which has the same result as performing action x and then performing action y, then the system is described by the table below.

∘	a	b
a	b	a
b	a	b

Note that $a \circ a$ means "reverse the switch and then reverse it again," which has the same result as b, "not reversing the switch." Similarly, $a \circ b = a$, etc. This switching system has the same properties that we observed before. For example, in this system the binary operation ∘ is *commutative;* that is,

$$x \circ y = y \circ x$$

for any replacement of x and y by a or b. The reader should decide whether the operation is also *associative;* that is, whether

$$x \circ (y \circ z) = (x \circ y) \circ z.$$

It is interesting to note that b is an *identity* element for ∘ in this system because

$$b \circ a = a \circ b = a \qquad \text{and} \qquad b \circ b = b.$$

Does every element of this system have an inverse under ∘? What is an inverse of a under ∘? What is an inverse of b?

Another simple system can be constructed out of the arithmetic of odd and even integers. Let E, O be the elements of the set, and let $+$ symbolize the operation defined by the table:

$+$	E	O
E	E	O
O	O	E

(An even integer added to an even integer yields an even integer, etc. Here the operation $+$ is not quite the same as the usual addition of numbers. Nor are E and O numbers themselves; they are symbols for classes of numbers. The equation $E + O = O$, for example, means that the sum of *any* even and *any* odd numbers is some odd number.) It is left for the reader to verify that the properties of this system are exactly the same as those of the system of switching actions.

These two systems are, in effect, two different models of one abstract system consisting of a set of two elements and one binary operation defined by

$*$	e	f
e	f	e
f	e	f

where e and f are arbitrary symbols for the elements and $*$ the symbol for the binary operation. What is of algebraic concern here is not that the elements and operation can be given various physical or numerical interpretations (although this is of prime interest in applications), but rather that the three tables have an identical structure. Hence, whatever properties we discover in the abstract (e, f)-system are guaranteed to hold for any model of the system.

Group. The abstract systems discussed above were selected to illustrate the type of abstract system called a *group*.

> Given any set S of elements and one binary operation $*$ on elements of S, the system $(S, *)$ is a *group* if it has the following properties:
>
> (1) For any elements x and y in S, $x * y$ is in S. (S is *closed* under $*$.)
> (2) For any elements x, y and z in S,
>
> $$x * (y * z) = (x * y) * z.$$
>
> ($*$ is *associative*.)

(3) There is an element i in S such that

$$x * i = i * x = x$$

for every x in S. (There is an *identity* for *.)

(4) Corresponding to each element x in S there is an element x' in S such that

$$x * x' = x' * x = i.$$

(Each element has an *inverse* under *.)

Thus, the first system we discussed, $(T, \oplus)$, is a group; it also has the additional property of commutativity and is therefore called a *commutative*, or *abelian*, group. The system consisting of the set of all integers and the binary operation of addition is also an abelian group, as the reader should verify. On the other hand, the system consisting of the set of all integers and the operation of multiplication is not a group because it lacks one of the required properties. (Which one?)

Are there any other properties that all groups have in common? Let us list several such properties and discuss their implications.

Let a, b, c be elements of any group, with * representing the binary operation and e the identity element. Then

(a) if $a = b$ then $a * c = b * c$; if $a = b$, then $c * a = c * b$;

(b) if $a * c = b * c$, then $a = b$; if $c * a = c * b$, then $a = b$; that is, cancellation can be done on the right or on the left;

(c) if $e_1 * a = a$ and $e_2 * a = a$ for all a, then $e_1 = e_2$; that is, the identity is unique;

(d) if $a' * a = e$ and $a'' * a = e$, then $a' = a''$; that is, the inverse of each element is unique.

Property (a) is a reminder that in general the operation of a group is not commutative and that a symbol must name exactly one element. If a and b are two names for an element of a group, then $a * c$ and $b * c$ are two names for one particular element; $c * a$ and $c * b$ are two names for possibly a different element unless * is commutative.

Property (b) states that formal cancellation may be performed on the left or on the right in an equation. Note that $a * c = c * b$ does *not* imply $a = b$. We prove Property (b) as follows.

Proof. If $a * c = b * c$, then $(a * c) * c' = (b * c) * c'$, where c' is an inverse of c. Then

$$a * (c * c') = b * (c * c'), \qquad \text{by associativity of } *,$$
$$a * e = b * e, \qquad \text{by definition of inverse,}$$
$$a = b, \qquad \text{by definition of identity.}$$

How may this proof be changed to prove that if $c * a = c * b$, then $a = b$?

The definition of a group requires that there be an identity for the operation, but it does not say how many identities there might be. Property (c) says that a group has exactly one identity for the operation.

Proof. Assume that there are two identities, e_1 and e_2, such that for all elements a of the group,

$$e_1 * a = a \quad \text{and} \quad e_2 * a = a.$$

Then $e_1 * a$ and $e_2 * a$ are two names for a, so that

$$e_1 * a = e_2 * a.$$

Hence

$$e_1 = e_2, \quad \text{by right cancellation, Property (b).}$$

Each element of a group has an inverse, and Property (d) says that there is exactly one such inverse.

Proof. Assume that element a has two inverses, a' and a''. Then, by definition of an inverse,

$$a' * a = e \quad \text{and} \quad a'' * a = e.$$

Since e is unique by Property (c), it follows that $a' * a$ and $a'' * a$ are two names for the identity, and

$$a' * a = a'' * a.$$

Then, by right cancellation,

$$a' = a''.$$

This completes the proof.

Ring. In some systems, such as the additive group of integers, it is natural to define a second operation on the elements. Under certain conditions on the second operation we have a system called a *ring*.

Let $(S, \oplus)$ be a commutative group and let $\odot$ be another binary operation in S. Then $(S, \oplus, \odot)$ is a *ring* if:

(a) S is closed under $\odot$,
(b) $\odot$ is associative, and
(c) $\odot$ is distributive through $\oplus$, that is,

$$a \odot (b \oplus c) = (a \odot b) \oplus (a \odot c),$$
$$(b \oplus c) \odot a = (b \odot a) \oplus (c \odot a),$$

for every element a, b, c in S.

We see immediately that the set I of integers with ordinary addition $+$ and multiplication $\cdot$ is a ring. In fact, the system $(I, +, \cdot)$ has some additional properties not required in a ring:

the integers have an *identity* 1 for $\cdot$, so that

$$a \cdot 1 = 1 \cdot a = a \quad \text{for all } a \text{ in } I;$$

and $\cdot$ is *commutative*, that is,

$$a \cdot b = b \cdot a \quad \text{for all } a, b \text{ in } I.$$

Thus, $(I, +, \cdot)$ is a *commutative ring* with *multiplicative identity*. In problems 9 through 11 we encounter noncommutative rings and rings without multiplicative identities. Another property of the system of integers is one which not all rings possess, namely, there are no nonzero elements of I that are zero divisors. See problem 17.

In Chapter 3 we shall consider systems with two operations, called *fields*, which are more specialized than rings. The study of the properties of rings and fields is central to an understanding of elementary algebra.

EXERCISE GROUP 1-2

1. Consider the set of elements $\{E, O\}$ and the binary operations $+$, $\times$ defined by:

$+$	E	O		$\times$	E	O
E	E	O		E	E	E
O	O	E		O	E	O

Show that the operation $\times$ is commutative. Is there an identity element for $\times$ in this set? Determine whether $\times$ is *distributive* through $+$, that is, whether

$$x \times (y + z) = (x \times y) + (x \times z)$$

for any replacements of E or O for x, y, z. Is $+$ distributive through $\times$?

2. Consider the system consisting of the set of elements $\{r, s, t\}$ and the binary operations $\circ$ and $*$ defined by the tables:

$\circ$	r	s	t		$*$	r	s	t
r	r	s	t		r	t	s	r
s	s	t	r		s	r	t	s
t	t	r	s		t	s	r	t

Is the set closed under ∘? under *? Is the operation ∘ commutative? Is * commutative? Is there an identity for ∘? for *? Is ∘ distributive through *? Is * distributive through ∘? Does every element have an inverse under ∘?

3. Let the elements of a set of actions be:

   A: rotating an equilateral triangle 120° clockwise about its center in its plane;

   B: rotating the equilateral triangle 240° clockwise about its center in its plane;

   C: not moving the triangle.

Let $x \circ y$ be the action which has the same result as first performing action x and then performing action y. Construct a table showing all results of the operation. Does this set and this binary operation form a mathematical system? If so, is the set closed under ∘? Is the operation ∘ commutative? associative? Is there an identity element for the operation? Does every element have an inverse under ∘? Is this system a group? Is it a commutative group?

4. Consider the set X of six actions consisting of rotations and reflections of an equilateral triangle (Fig. 1–1).

I: no action

R_1: rotation in the plane 120° clockwise about the center

R_2: rotation in the plane 240° clockwise about the center

S_1: reflection about axis 1

S_2: reflection about axis 2

S_3: reflection about axis 3

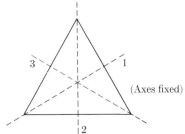

(Axes fixed)

FIGURE 1–1

If x, y are any actions in X, let $x \circ y$ be the action that has the same result as performing x and then y, in that order. From the example illustrated in Fig. 1–2, it follows that $R_1 \circ S_2 = S_3$.

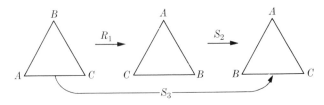

FIGURE 1–2

Fill in the table below, where the first action is listed in the left column and the second action in the top row. Show that the system $(X, \circ)$ is a group. Is it a commutative group? What is the identity for ∘? What is the inverse of S_2? If x' represents the inverse of x, determine

(a) $(S_1 \circ R_2)'$

(b) $R_2' \circ S_1'$

(c) $(R_1 \circ S_3) \circ (S_3' \circ R_2)$

(d) $(S_1' \circ S_2) \circ (S_3' \circ S_1)$

∘	I	R_1	R_2	S_1	S_2	S_3
I						
R_1						
R_2						
S_1						
S_2	S_1					
S_3						

5. Consider the set $\{1, 2, 3, 4\}$ and the operation $\odot$ defined as follows: for any elements a, b in the set, $a \odot b$ is the remainder when the product of a and b is divided by 5. For example, $3 \odot 4 = 2$, $4 \odot 4 = 1$, etc. Is the resulting system a group?

6. Determine whether the set $\{a, b, c, d\}$ and the operation ‡ as defined by the following table are a group.

‡	a	b	c	d
a	b	d	a	c
b	d	c	b	a
c	a	b	c	d
d	c	a	d	b

If not, what properties are lacking? (The operation ‡ *is* associative, although it would require 4^3 cases to verify this fact. The reader should check a few random cases before he accepts this statement.)

7. Determine whether the set $\{r, s, u, v\}$ and the operation $++$, as defined by the following table, are a group.

$++$	r	s	u	v
r	r	s	u	v
s	s	r	v	u
u	u	v	r	r
v	v	u	s	s

If not, what properties are lacking?

8. Let a, b, c be any elements of a group $(S, *)$, and let the inverse of an element a be denoted by a', and the identity by e. Prove:

(a) $(a')' = a$. [*Hint*: $a' * a = a * a'$.]

(b) $(a * b)' = b' * a'$. [*Hint*: $x' = y$ means $y * x = x * y = e$.]

(c) Every equation of the form $x * a = b$ or $a * y = b$ has a unique solution x or y, respectively, in S.

(d) If $a * a = e$ for all a in S, then $(S, *)$ is a commutative group.

9. Consider the set E of all even integers with $+$ and $\cdot$. Is $(E, +, \cdot)$ a ring? Is there an identity for $\cdot$?

10. Decide in each case whether the system $(S, +)$ is a group; whether $(S, +, \cdot)$ is a ring. If not, what properties are lacking?

(a) $S = \{0\}$.

(b) $S =$ set of all integral multiples of 4.

(c) $S =$ set of all numbers $a + b\sqrt{2}$, where a and b are integers.

11. Let M be the set of all *matrices* of the form

$$\begin{pmatrix} a & b \\ c & d \end{pmatrix},$$

where a, b, c, d are integers, and define

$$\begin{pmatrix} a & b \\ c & d \end{pmatrix} = \begin{pmatrix} a' & b' \\ c' & d' \end{pmatrix}$$

if and only if

$$a = a', \qquad b = b', \qquad c = c', \qquad d = d',$$

$$\begin{pmatrix} a & b \\ c & d \end{pmatrix} \oplus \begin{pmatrix} a' & b' \\ c' & d' \end{pmatrix} = \begin{pmatrix} a + a' & b + b' \\ c + c' & d + d' \end{pmatrix},$$

$$\begin{pmatrix} a & b \\ c & d \end{pmatrix} \odot \begin{pmatrix} a' & b' \\ c' & d' \end{pmatrix} = \begin{pmatrix} aa' + bc' & ab' + bd' \\ ca' + dc' & cb' + dd' \end{pmatrix}.$$

Verify that $(M, \oplus, \odot)$ is a ring. Does it have an identity for $\odot$? Is it a commutative ring?

12. Consider the set $T = \{0, 1, 2, 3\}$ and the operations $\oplus$, $\odot$ defined as follows:

$a \oplus b$ is the remainder when $a + b$ is divided by 4;

$a \odot b$ is the remainder when ab is divided by 4.

Decide whether $(T, \oplus, \odot)$ is a ring; a commutative ring. What is the inverse of 2 under $\oplus$? under $\odot$?

13. Prove that if a is any element in the ring $(S, \oplus, \odot)$, then

$$a \odot 0 = 0 \odot a = 0,$$

where 0 is the identity for $\oplus$. [*Hint:* Consider $b \oplus 0 = b$, where b is an element of S. Then $a \odot (b \oplus 0) = a \odot b$. Now apply the distributive property.]

14. (a) Do the odd integers form a group with respect to addition?

(b) Do the integers of the form $5k$, k an integer, form a group with respect to addition? with respect to multiplication?

(c) Let $a * b = a - b$, where a, b are integers. Do the integers form a group with respect to the operation $*$?

(d) Let $a \odot b$ be the remainder upon dividing ab by 4, where a, b are elements of the set $T = \{0, 1, 2, 3\}$. Is $(T, \odot)$ a group?

(e) Let $a \,\#\, b$ be the remainder upon dividing ab by 10, where a, b are any elements of the set $Q = \{1, 3, 7, 9\}$. Is $(Q, \#)$ a group?

15. Consider a set S of elements and a binary operation $*$ such that S is closed under $*$ and $*$ is associative. Let there be an element e of S for which $e * a = a$ for all a in S (e is called a *left identity* for $*$). For each a in S let there be an element a' in S such that $a' * a = e$ (a' is a *left inverse* of a). Show that under these conditions $(S, *)$ is a group. In other words, prove the following sequence of theorems:

(a) *Left cancellation:* If $a * b = a * c$, then $b = c$.

(b) *Left identity is a right identity:* If $e * a = a$ for all a, then $a * e = a$. [*Hint:* $a' * a = e = e * e = (a' * a) * e = a' * (a * e)$; then apply left cancellation.]

(c) *Left inverse is a right inverse:* If $a' * a = e$, then $a * a' = e$. [*Hint:* $a' * (a * a') = (a' * a) * a' = e * a' = a' * e$; then apply left cancellation.]

(d) *Right cancellation:* If $b * a = c * a$, then $b = c$.

(e) *Uniqueness of left identity.*

(f) *Uniqueness of left inverses.*

16. Problem 4 provides an example of a noncommutative group. Give examples from the group $(X, \circ)$ of problem 4 to show that:

(a) $x \circ y = y \circ z$ does not imply $x = z$;

(b) $(x \circ y)' \neq x' \circ y'$;

(c) a right inverse of x is a left inverse of x;

(d) if $x = y$, then $z \circ x \neq y \circ z$.

17. If r is an element of a ring and $r \neq 0$ (denoting the identity for the first operation by 0), we say that r is a *proper divisor of zero* if

$$r \cdot s = s \cdot r = 0$$

for some s in the ring, $s \neq 0$ (where the second operation is denoted by $\cdot$). In other words, proper divisors of zero are nonzero elements whose product (result of the second operation) is zero. Consider the rings described in problems 11 and 12. Does either of these rings contain proper divisors of zero?

18. Let D be the set of all ordered pairs of integers (p, q) such that

$$\begin{aligned} (p, q) &= (r, s) \qquad \text{if and only if} \qquad ps = qr, \\ (p, q) \oplus (r, s) &= (p + r, q + s), \\ (p, q) \odot (r, s) &= (pr, qs). \end{aligned}$$

We know that the ring of integers has no proper divisors of zero. Verify that the system $(D, \oplus, \odot)$ is a ring that has proper divisors of zero.

1–3. COMMENTS ON THE TEACHING OF ALGEBRA

Unfortunately, a description of a specific model of an abstract system gives young students little understanding of the system. They learn many facts about real numbers—this is an important part of their education— but these facts in themselves do not significantly contribute to an understanding of the real number system.

Although the breakthrough to modern algebra came approximately a hundred years ago, to many school children the word "algebra" still means a collection of isolated tricks—devices specifically designed for handling individual situations. The traditional textbook is full of symptoms of this attitude. There are, for example, boxes which emphasize the "how to," or hands pointing to the rule that must be remembered. Some students see for themselves a bit of the structure underlying these tricks, and others enjoy the sheer fun of getting the right "answers" to the manipulations. But for the vast majority of students, it is a matter of memorizing a set of symbolic commands, often in the form of "four-step" methods or "rules of signs," etc.

Fortunately, the algebra taught in the schools is for the most part mathematically important. The student does need the skills of "symbol pushing" for his later mathematical studies. Hence it should not be the aim of a new program to change this aspect drastically. However, we wish to make the point that every bit of manipulation which we teach, and which the student must be able to do, is valid *for a reason*. There is a mathematical truth about, say, real numbers, or about polynomials, which is behind every symbol we move around, and we must teach these truths to make algebra meaningful and exciting to the student. Thus a new program must aim not only at the usual skills but also at an understanding and appreciation of the structure of the real number system, and to a lesser extent, of polynomials. A multitude of exercises is still absolutely necessary for gaining manipulative facility, but these techniques must be tied to the ideas from which they derive their validity. Thus, when algebra is taught through an understanding of the real number system, there need be little memorizing of "rules." The ideas learned through understanding can be rediscovered when they are needed.

The teacher of new materials must ask himself (not his students) the following questions: What is the abstract system of which the set of real numbers with addition and multiplication is a model? What are the structural properties of this system? How do these properties motivate and unify the solutions of equations and operations on algebraic expressions and functions? We shall try to provide some answers in later chapters.

The teaching of algebra has two equally important aspects: to give the student a glimpse of the structure of the subject *and* to treat the language with great care. Statements which record the properties of a mathematical system depend on concise language. Distinguishing between "and" and "or," "if" and "only if," "not" and "none," etc., is crucial to understanding. We will discuss this further in Chapter 2. Language also involves choices of descriptive words. Unlike the chemist, who uses long compound words to describe his materials, the mathematician often selects common words to describe uncommon concepts. The teacher should be wary of dictionary meanings for words such as rational, real, imaginary, complex, group, ring, field, limit, term, factor, domain, and range. Used as mathematical terms, such words do *not* have the meanings commonly ascribed to them.

In the following chapters, we shall be concerned with the precise structure of an abstract system called a *complete ordered field* because it has as a model the real number system. Then we shall dissect this system into subsystems and examine each in search of its relations to the system and to other subsystems. In this way we may begin to see what underlies elementary algebra.

Chapter 2

Language of Elementary Algebra

2–1. THE ROLE OF SETS

The role of sets in teaching elementary algebra has generated heated arguments. Some would consider a course in algebra "modern" if it mentions the word "set"; others maintain that sets produce an unnecessary confusion.

Let us agree that the study of sets for their own sake probably does not belong in an elementary algebra course. On the other hand, the study of a mathematical system is a study of the properties of certain operations on the elements of some *set*. Thus, a set itself is of little interest in mathematics. It is the operations defined on the elements of the set that are of interest.* For example, a child easily learns to identify the elements of the set of whole numbers, but he begins to do arithmetic only when he learns to perform operations on these elements. Hence our study of systems must involve at least the language of sets.

We shall think of a *set* as a collection of objects. The objects, or *elements*, in a set have at least one common characteristic—all belong to the same set. This is not double-talk. For example, if the set is "my family," it is significant to say that a person x belongs to my family. The set of integers,

$$\{2, 4, 6, 8\},$$

has four elements, each of which happens to be an even integer. But these four numbers constitute a set merely because they have been listed together. The point is that often we are concerned with a set rather than with its individual elements. Thus, a line is a set of points, but we may think of the line as one entity, or even as an element of a set of lines. In fact, much of mathematics deals with sets of sets of sets of sets . . .

Just as it is possible to describe a number with various names, such as

$$5 - 2 = 3 = \tfrac{6}{2} = \sqrt{9} = \cdots,$$

---

* Formal set theory may be thought of as a study of operations on the subsets of a set; the elements of the set are themselves sets.

so it is possible to describe a set in different ways:

$$\{2, 4, 6, 8\} = \{4, 8, 6, 2\}$$
$$= A : \text{the set of even positive integers less than 10}$$
$$= B : \text{the set of positive multiples of 2 which are less than 9.}$$

The $=$ sign has the usual meaning of equality:

$\frac{6}{2} = \sqrt{9}$ means "$\frac{6}{2}$ and $\sqrt{9}$ are two different names
for one particular number,"

and for sets A and B,

$A = B$ means "A and B are two different symbols
representing one particular set."

REMARK: Note that "$a = b$" is sometimes translated "the numbers a and b are equal." But this sentence does not really refer to two numbers; it is a statement about one number and two different names for that number. Equality used in this sense is a means of classifying numerals for numbers. It tells us when two numerals are equivalent (name the same number) and hence in the same class. For example, one class of numerals contains 3, $\sqrt{9}$, $\frac{6}{2}$, $5 - 2$, ... All the numerals in this class name the number "three."

What are the properties of $=$ when considered as a relation between numerals? (1) We obviously have $a = a$, since the numeral "a" can name only one number. (2) Also, if $a = b$, then certainly $b = a$. (3) If $a = b$ and $b = c$ then "a" and "c" name the same number and $a = c$. These three properties describe the equivalence of numerals; in fact, we take these three properties to be the definition of equivalence among elements of any set.

If p, q, r are any elements of a set X and $\sim$ is a relation between pairs of elements of X, then we say $\sim$ is an *equivalence* in X if

E1 (reflexive property): $p \sim p$.
E2 (symmetric property): if $p \sim q$, then $q \sim p$.
E3 (transitive property): if $p \sim q$ and $q \sim r$, then $p \sim r$.

There are many relations that are equivalences; for example, "congruence" for triangles, "same slope" for lines. Some relations are not equivalences; for example, "perpendicular" for lines is "the brother of" for people.

The effect of an equivalence in a set is to *partition* (sort) the elements of the set into classes, each class containing elements equivalent to one another. These classes are *disjoint*, no class having an element in common with any other class. (Note that in the definitions of groups and rings in Chapter 1 we tacitly assumed that the relation "$=$" is an equivalence.)

If a set A is described by listing its elements in a roster, we enclose its elements within braces. If A is described by stating its characteristics, we must be certain that the description allows us to determine without ambiguity whether an element belongs to the set. "All the whole numbers I can write" does not suffice to define a set unless it is known how much energy and time I have, how long my writing equipment will hold out, and in what order I propose to write the numbers. "All the whole numbers greater than 3 and less than 4" does define a set, namely the *null* or *empty* set, the set with *no* elements, symbolized by $\emptyset$.

Beginning algebra students bring with them a good deal of information about two sets: the set A of numbers of arithmetic (the nonnegative real numbers) and the set P of points on a line. Each of these has interesting subsets.

> If every element of a set S belongs to a set T, then S is a *subset* of T, and we say that S is contained in T, written $S \subset T$.

Thus the set W of whole numbers $\{0, 1, 2, 3, \ldots\}$ is a subset of the set A of the numbers of arithmetic, $W \subset A$. It should be noted that a set is always a subset of itself.

> If S is a subset of T, there are two possibilities: (1) $S = T$, or (2) S is a proper subset of T.
>
> (1) $S = T$ if $S \subset T$ and $T \subset S$.
> (2) S is a *proper* subset of T if $S \subset T$ and $S \neq T$.

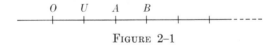

FIGURE 2–1

Let us consider a line and two distinct points O and U on the line, with U to the right of O. Then take the distance between O and U as a unit measure and mark on the line to the right of U the point A that is a unit distance from U; then the point B to the right of A a unit distance from A; etc. The set M of points so marked is a proper subset of the set P of all points on the line. An important fact in algebra is that there exists a relationship between the set M of equispaced points and the set W of whole numbers. We say that there exists a correspondence between these two sets; indeed, there are many such correspondences.

> Given two sets S and T, whenever there is a rule which determines pairs of elements, the first element of each pair from S and the second element from T, there is a *correspondence* between S and T.

(a) $(O, 0), (U, 2), (A, 4), (B, 6), \ldots$

O	U	A	B	$C \cdots$
0	2	4	6	$8 \cdots$

(b) $(O, 0), (U, 0), (A, 1), (B, 1), (C, 2), \ldots$

O	U	A	B	$C \cdots$
0	0	1	1	$2 \cdots$

(c) $(O, 3), (U, 3), (A, 3), (B, 3), \ldots$

O	U	A	B	$C \cdots$
3	3	3	3	$3 \cdots$

(d) $(O, 0), (U, 1), (U, 2), (A, 3), (A, 4), \ldots$

O	U	A	B	$C \cdots$
0	1,2	3,4	5,6	$7,8 \cdots$

(e) $(O, 0), (U, 1), (A, 2), (B, 3), (C, 4), \ldots$

O	U	A	B	$C \cdots$
0	1	2	3	$4 \cdots$

FIGURE 2-2

Let us examine a few of the many possible correspondences between $M = \{O, U, A, B, C, D, \ldots\}$ and $W = \{0, 1, 2, 3, 4, \ldots\}$. Note that our definition of correspondence requires that elements of M be paired with elements of W in such a way that the first element of each pair is an element of M and the second is an element of W (Fig. 2–2).

Some of the above correspondences pair off each element of M with exactly one element of W; we shall call such a correspondence *single-valued*. Other names we shall use are: *mapping* and *function*. Thus all the above correspondences except (d) are mappings; (d) is a *multiple-valued* correspondence, because at least one element of M is paired with more than one element of W. Note that (c) is a mapping in which every element of M is paired with the same element of W; we call this a *constant* mapping.

It is convenient to denote a mapping with a letter; thus $f: M \rightarrow W$ denotes the mapping f which "maps the set M into the set W."

Some of the above correspondences involve *all* the elements of W. A mapping of this sort is called an *onto* mapping, since the set of second elements of the pairs is the whole set W. We see that (b) and (e) are onto mappings. On the other hand, (a) and (c) are not onto. All mappings are *into* in the sense that the second elements of the pairs form a subset of W. The reader should determine the proper subsets of W for (a) and (c).

Given a correspondence between M and W, we may form its *inverse* correspondence between W and M by interchanging the elements of the pairs. For example, the mapping $b: M \rightarrow W$ determines the pairs

$$(O, 0), (U, 0), (A, 1), (B, 1), (C, 2), (D, 2), \ldots$$

Its inverse correspondence determines the pairs

$$(0, O), (0, U), (1, A), (1, B), (2, C), (2, D), \ldots$$

We now ask: is this inverse correspondence of the mapping (b) also a mapping? We see that it is not because it is multiple-valued.

In most of our discussion we shall be concerned with mappings whose inverse correspondences are also mappings. Note that among the above correspondences, (a), (b), (c), and (e) are mappings, and the inverses of (a) and (e) are also mappings. If f is a mapping whose inverse correspondence is a mapping, we indicate its inverse mapping by f^{-1}; such a mapping is called one-to-one.

> A correspondence between sets S and T is called *one-to-one* (1–1) if both the correspondence and its inverse correspondence are onto mappings.

Again let us refer back to the examples of correspondences between M and W:

(d) is not a mapping;

(c) is a mapping of M into, not onto W;

(b) is a mapping of M onto W;

(a) is a mapping of M into, not onto W;

(e) is a 1–1 mapping of M onto W; that is, a 1–1 correspondence between M and W.

FIGURE 2–3

It is natural that among these five different types of correspondences we should choose (e) as the one to be used in labeling the points of M on the line. We say that each element of M (a marked point on the line) has a *coordinate* which is the whole number in W associated with it under the 1–1 onto mapping (e). Thus, each marked point has exactly one coordinate, and each whole number is the coordinate of exactly one point.

Although it is convenient to speak of these points and numbers interchangeably, such as "the point 2" when we mean "the point whose coordinate is 2," it must be remembered that the set M is *not equal* to the set W. They are quite different sets.

We have avoided the necessity of listing a roster of the elements of W by writing

$$W = \{0, 1, 2, 3, \ldots\}$$

to indicate that each element has a *successor* and, hence, there is no "last element" of W. This is an example of an infinite set, where we intuitively think of "infinity" in terms of "no end."

Intuition, however, is not to be trusted. It would be better to describe an infinite set in some manner which does not involve the elusive "no end." For instance, note that there exists a proper subset of W, the set E of all even whole numbers,

$$E = \{0, 2, 4, 6, \ldots\},$$

such that there is a one-to-one correspondence between E and the set W. We indicate the pairings of elements of this one-to-one correspondence as follows:

$$
\begin{array}{cc}
E & W \\
0 & \leftrightarrow 0 \\
2 & \leftrightarrow 1 \\
4 & \leftrightarrow 2 \\
6 & \leftrightarrow 3 \\
\vdots & \vdots
\end{array}
$$

We could exhibit many one-to-one correspondences between E and W. The point to be made is that there does exist one such correspondence.

Some experimenting with finite sets will suggest that a one-to-one correspondence between a set and a proper subset of itself is not possible with a finite number of elements available. Take, for example, the set

$$\{1, 2, 3, \ldots, 100\}$$

and try to find a proper subset and a 1–1 correspondence between the set and the subset.

This example suggests a more satisfactory definition of an infinite set.

A set T is *infinite* if for some proper subset S of T there exists a one-to-one correspondence between T and S.

We define a set to be *finite* if it is not infinite; that is, a finite set *cannot* be put in one-to-one correspondence with a proper subset of itself.

Now that we have established that the set W of whole numbers is infinite, we can show that the set of points M is infinite as a consequence of the one-to-one correspondence between W and M.

Some infinite sets have the property of being *countable*; that is, they are in one-to-one correspondence with the set of counting numbers. Later we shall deal with infinite sets which are not countable, such as the set R of all real numbers.

Much of our attention in later chapters will be directed to the fundamental one-to-one correspondence between the set of *all* the points of a line and the set R of *all* real numbers. This correspondence is at the heart of coordinate geometry—the properties of points on the line suggest analogous properties of real numbers, and vice versa.

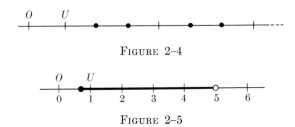

FIGURE 2–4

FIGURE 2–5

To bring out this intimate relation between sets of points and sets of numbers, we use special language and symbolism to connect them. We call the number paired with a point under a given 1–1 correspondence, the *coordinate* of the point. The set of points corresponding to a certain set of numbers is called the *graph* of the set of numbers. For example, the set of points indicated by heavy dots in Fig. 2–4 is the graph of the set {2, 3, 5, 6}. The graph of A, where

$$A = \text{set of all real numbers less than 5 and}$$
$$\text{greater than or equal to } \tfrac{2}{3},$$

is indicated in Fig. 2–5 by a heavy line and solid dot.

EXERCISE GROUP 2–1

1. Given the sets:

$A = \{\tfrac{8}{6}, \sqrt{\tfrac{9}{4}}, \tfrac{5}{3}\}$
$B = $ set of all negative integers greater than 3
$C = $ set of all whole numbers which are not multiples of 3
$D = $ set of all rational numbers between 1 and 2 named by fractions with denominators "2" or "3"
$E = \{0\}$
$F = $ set of all rational numbers between 1 and 2 named by fractions with numerators "2", "3", "4", or "5"
$G = $ set of all whole numbers which are multiples of 3
$H = $ set of all numbers x such that $x^2 + x = x$
$J = $ set of all numbers of the form $3x + 1$ or $3x + 2$, where x is any whole number

Decide which of these sets are equal; for which pairs can a one-to-one correspondence be defined?

2. Which of the sets in problem 1 are proper subsets of the set W of whole numbers? of the set G in problem 1?

3. Consider the correspondence between S and T, where the sets S and T and the rule of correspondence are defined in each of the problems below. In each case exhibit several pairs and describe the correspondence fully in terms of "mapping," "into," "onto," "one-to-one." Let I denote the set of integers, R the set of real numbers, and L the set $\{-1, 0, 1\}$.

S	T	Rule of correspondence
(a) I	I	x in S, $\quad x \to -x$
(b) I	I	x in S, $\quad x \to x^2$
(c) I	R	To each element x in S there corresponds y in T such that $x + y = 7$.
(d) R	R	To each x in S there corresponds y in T such that $x^2 = y^2$.
(e) R	R	To each x in S there corresponds y in T such that $x^2 = y^3$.
(f) L	L	To each x in S there corresponds y in T such that $|x| + y = 1$.
(g) L	L	To each x in S there corresponds y in T such that $x + |y| = 1$.
(h) L	L	To each x in S there corresponds y in T such that $|x| + |y| = 1$.

4. Which of the following sets are infinite?

    (a) Set C of problem 1

    (b) Set D of problem 1

    (c) Set of all positive rational numbers named by fractions with denominator 3

    (d) Set of all numbers of the form $a\sqrt{2}$, where a is an integer

    (e) The set of all rational numbers between 3 and 5 named by fractions with denominators "3" or "4."

5. In Chapter 1 we described binary operations on a set. Such operations can be thought of as correspondences, as follows.

Given a set S, construct the set U consisting of all possible pairs of elements of S such that if a, b are in S, then (a, b) is an element of U (U is called the *cartesian product* of S and S and is usually written $S \times S$). Now define a mapping b of U onto some set T, $b\colon U \to T$; that is, to each pair (a, b) in U there corresponds exactly one element of T. Such a mapping is called a binary operation on S.

    (a) If W is the set of whole numbers, describe the mappings that define ordinary addition and ordinary multiplication. What is the set T in these cases?

    (b) A *unary* operation on a set S is a mapping of S onto some set T. Given that S is the set of all positive real numbers, describe the mappings which define the operations of squaring and of extracting the square root. What is the set T in these cases?

6. If f is a binary operation on the set S, $f\colon S \times S \to T$, and if T is a subset of S, we say that S is *closed* under the operation f. (It is not necessary that T be a proper subset of S.) Decide whether the following sets are closed under the indicated binary operations.

(a)	All whole numbers which are not multiples of 3	Multiplication
(b)	All whole numbers which are not multiples of 4	Multiplication
(c)	$\{0, 1\}$	Multiplication
(d)	$\{0, 1\}$	Addition
(e)	All positive integers	Subtraction
(f)	All positive rational numbers	Division
(g)	All positive integers	Half the sum
(h)	All even integers	Half the product
(i)	All squares of integers	Addition
(j)	All rational numbers between 0 and 1	Multiplication

With what mathematical facts do you associate the answers to (a) and (b)?

A *unary* operation is performed on a single element. Decide whether the sets are closed under the unary operations indicated below.

(k) All positive rational numbers   Square root
(l) All integers   Squaring
(m) All even integers   Half the square

7. The system $(T, \oplus)$ defined on p. 3 and the system $(S, *)$ defined on p. 4 were said to have the same structure. By this we shall mean that $(S, *)$ and $(T, \oplus)$ are *isomorphic* (written $S \cong T$); that is, there exists a one-to-one mapping f of S onto T such that if s_1, s_2 are in S and if f pairs s_1 with t_1, s_2 with t_2, where t_1, t_2 are in T, then f pairs $s_1 * s_2$ with $t_1 \oplus t_2$ (Fig. 2–6). In other words, an isomorphism is a one-to-one onto mapping which preserves the operation.

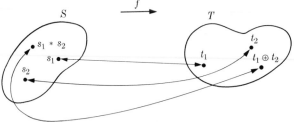

FIGURE 2–6

Decide which, if any, of the following systems are isomorphic, and describe the relevant mappings.

$(T, \oplus)$, as defined on p. 3
$(D, \circ)$, where D is the set of four rotations of a square about its center
$(G, \cdot)$, where $G = \{1, -1, i, -i\}$ and $\cdot$ is multiplication ($i \cdot i = -1$)
$(I, +)$, where I is the set of integers
$(E, +)$, where E is the set of even integers

8. Decide in each case whether the relation $\sim$ in the set X is an equivalence; if not, what properties are lacking?

$\sim$	X
(a) Is the cousin of	Set of people
(b) Is the same weight as	Set of men
(c) Is less than	Set of integers
(d) Is less than or equal to	Set of integers
(e) Lives in the same city as	Set of people
(f) Is the square of	Set of integers
(g) Has the same remainder upon division by 4	Set of integers
(h) Is a factor of	Set of integers

9. In problem 12 of Exercise Group 1–2, describe the relation between integers a and b as:

$$a = b \quad \text{means} \quad a - b = 4n \quad \text{for some integer } n,$$

and show that this relation is an equivalence which partitions the integers into the four classes represented by the elements of T.

10. In problem 11 of Exercise Group 1–2, show that the relation $=$ is an equivalence.

11. In problem 18 of Exercise Group 1–2, show that the relation $=$ is an equivalence.

2–2. MATHEMATICAL SENTENCES

The properties of an abstract system could be described and recorded in terms of English sentences. However, by abbreviating English sentences into mathematical sentences, you increase efficiency and avoid ambiguity. Thus we abbreviate the sentence

"Five plus three is nine."

to

$$5 + 3 = 9,$$

meaning, of course, that "$5 + 3$" and "9" are different symbols for the same number. There is no doubt that we have written an English sentence, but there may be some doubt about the corresponding mathematical sentence. It *is* a sentence, even though the statement it makes is false.

We shall be concerned with sentences or statements which we assume to be either *true* or *false*, but not both, and which have meaning and content. Any statement to which this assumption does not apply shall be excluded from our discussion. For example, "$4 =$ a triangle" has no meaning and will not be considered as a sentence. Also, "$3^+ - (\ ) = 2\sqrt{\ }$" makes no sense because it does not conform to accepted mathematical grammar. On the other hand, "Every positive even integer is the sum of two primes" is a sentence because, even though no one knows whether it is true, we are willing to accept it as either true or false. The assumptions that sentences are either true or false, but not both, are often called the laws of *excluded middle* and the *contradiction* of logic.

Simple sentences concerning numbers may involve any of the verb symbols $=, <, >, \neq, \nless, \ngtr$, which have the usual meanings of equality and order and their negations. Compound sentences are constructed from simple sentences by conjunction, disjunction, or conditional clauses.

If A, B are sentences, then the sentence

A and B (conjunction)

is true if both A and B are true; otherwise, it is false. The sentence

A or B (disjunction)

is false if both A and B are false; otherwise, it is true.

For example, the disjunction $5 < 6$ or $5 = 6$ (abbreviated $5 \leq 6$) is true because at least one of the sentences, namely "$5 < 6$," is true. But the conjunction $5 < 6$ and $5 = 6$ is false because at least one of the sentences, namely "$5 = 6$," is false.

If A is a sentence, then the sentence

$$\text{not-}A \quad (negation)$$

is true if A is false and is false if A is true.

Care should be taken to distinguish between sentences such as "not-$(A$ or $B)$" and "not-A or B." The first is the negation of a disjunction (is this a disjunction?), and the second is the disjunction of not-A with B. For example,

$$\text{not-}(5 > 6 \quad \text{or} \quad 5 \neq 6)$$

is false because "$5 > 6$ or $5 \neq 6$" is true. But

$$\text{not-}(5 > 6) \quad \text{or} \quad 5 \neq 6$$

is true, because "$5 \neq 6$" is true.

If A, B are sentences, then the sentence

$$\text{if } A, \text{ then } B \quad (conditional)$$

is false if A is true and B is false; otherwise, it is true.

For example, the conditional

$$\text{if} \quad 2 + 3 = 5, \quad \text{then} \quad 3 + 4 = 6$$

is false because the sentence $A: 2 + 3 = 5$ is true and the sentence $B: 3 + 4 = 6$ is false. On the other hand, the conditional

$$\text{if} \quad 2 + 3 = 4, \quad \text{then} \quad 3 + 4 = 7$$

is true because "$2 + 3 = 4$" is false and "$3 + 4 = 7$" is true.

At this point it is instructive to list the possibilities which, according to the definition, yield a true conditional.

A	B	if A, then B
True	True	True
False	True	True
False	False	True

The remaining possibility, namely, A true and B false, is the *only* one for which "if A, then B" is false.

At first thought this definition of a conditional seems to violate the common meaning of "if A, then B." Actually, this definition is motivated by our desire to express any valid reasoning leading from a sentence A to a sentence B. Certainly, if A is true, then any reasoning process that is valid will lead us from A to a true conclusion B. This is the first possibility listed in the above table. However, we must also acknowledge that if we argue from a false premise A and proceed by means of valid reasoning to a conclusion B, then B may sometimes be true and sometimes false. The emphasis is on the *validity* of the reasoning. For example, if we take as our premise $A : 5 = 4$, we may add 3 to both members to obtain B: $8 = 7$, which is false; we may, instead, remark that "$5 = 4$" and "$4 = 5$" yield $B : 5 + 4 = 4 + 5$, which is true. In each case, the reasoning was valid. Hence it is suggested that our definition of a true conditional include the second and third possibilities in the table. Of course, after we agree on a definition, we must forget the motivation which suggested it and accept the form of the conditional even when there is no apparent relation between the sentences A and B in the sentence "if A, then B."

We do not allow the fourth possibility to occur in a valid reasoning process. Thus we call the conditional false if a true A leads to a false B. This can be summed up by saying that the conditional "if A, then B" is true if A is false *or* B is true; it is false if A is true *and* B is false. Thus, we may take as an alternative definition:

The conditional "if A, then B" is the disjunction "not-A or B."

We write the sentence

$$A \quad \text{if and only if} \quad B \quad (biconditional)$$

as an abbreviation for the conjunction

$$(\text{if} \quad A, \quad \text{then} \quad B) \quad \text{and} \quad (\text{if} \quad B, \quad \text{then} \quad A).$$

Thus a biconditional is true if both A and B are true or if both A and B are false.

The question arises: Is the following a sentence?

$$x + 3 = 5.$$

The answer depends on the meaning of the symbol x. If we require that x be a symbol for a number but do not state that number specifically, then "$x + 3 = 5$" is an *open* sentence in the sense that the question of its truth is left open until we specify what number x is. We shall call the particular set of numbers to which x belongs the *domain* of x. Here we have the first example of a *variable*; a more detailed discussion will be presented in Chapter 7.

There is a close relationship among sentences in one variable, sets of real numbers, and sets of points on the number line. For example, if the domain of x is the set of all integers, then the open sentence

$$x \geq 1 \qquad \text{and} \qquad x < 5$$

(which is usually abbreviated to $1 \leq x < 5$) is true if x is any element of the set

$$\{1, 2, 3, 4\}.$$

This set has the graph

FIGURE 2–7

It is natural to call $\{1, 2, 3, 4\}$ the *truth set* (or *solution set*) of the sentence and the graph of this set the *graph* of the sentence.

> The *truth set* of a sentence in one variable is the set of all numbers, and only those numbers, in the domain of the variable which make the sentence true.

Thus an open sentence in one variable is a sorter which separates the domain of the variable into two subsets; one is the truth set of the sentence, and the other is the set of the remaining numbers.

Note the importance of specifying the domain of the variable. If for the sentence "$x \geq 1$ and $x < 5$" the domain is, instead, the set of all real numbers, then its graph is

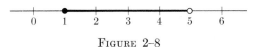

FIGURE 2–8

It is instructive to compare the graphs of the three sentences "$x \geq 1$," "$x < 5$," and "$x \geq 1$ and $x < 5$," where the domain of x is, say, the set of all positive real numbers. We see that the graph of "$x \geq 1$ and $x < 5$" consists of all the points which are in both the graph of "$x \geq 1$" *and* the graph of "$x < 5$."

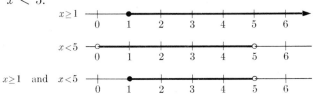

FIGURE 2–9

FIGURE 2–10

If S and T are sets, the set of elements, each of which belongs to both S and T, is the *intersection* of S and T.

Consider in Fig. 2–10 the sentences "$x \leq 1$," "$x > 5$," and "$x \leq 1$ or $x > 5$," where the domain of x is the set of all real numbers. The graph of "$x \leq 1$ or $x > 5$" contains all the points which belong to either the graph of "$x \leq 1$" *or* to the graph of "$x > 5$."

The set of elements, each of which belongs to either S or T, is the *union* of S and T.

As another example consider the open sentence

$$\text{if} \quad y \leq 3, \quad \text{then } y > 5, \quad y \text{ any integer.}$$

The truth set of this open sentence must contain all the integers greater than 3 (since for these integers the sentence "$y \leq 3$" is false); it must also contain all the integers greater than 5 (since for these integers the sentence "$y > 5$" is true). Hence, the truth set is the set of all integers greater than 3.

Consider the open sentences,

(1)   if $r < 3$,   then $4 = 2$, r any integer,

(2)   if $3 = 5$,   then $q = 1$, q any integer.

Since in sentence (1), $B: 4 = 2$ is false for all integers, the conditional is true only for those integers for which $A: r < 3$ is false, that is, for r greater than or equal to 3. In sentence (2), $A: 3 = 5$ is false for all integers; hence, the conditional is true for all integers.

A sentence in *two* ordered variables has a truth set consisting of a set of ordered *pairs* of numbers, the first number of each pair corresponding to the first variable and the second number to the second variable, such that these pairs and only these pairs make the sentence true. For example, if x (the first variable) and y have as domains the set of positive integers, then the sentence

$$x + y = 5$$

has the truth set

$$\{(1, 4), \quad (2, 3), \quad (3, 2), \quad (4, 1)\}.$$

The graph of a set of ordered pairs of numbers is the set of points on a plane located with respect to two perpendicular number lines as follows: if the number lines coincide at their O points, the number pair (a, b) corresponds to a point P whose projection on the first line has coordinate a and whose projection on the other line has coordinate b. For example, the graph of the sentence

$$x < y \quad \text{and} \quad y < 1,$$

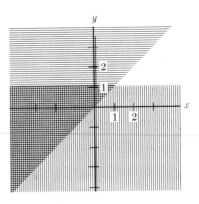

FIGURE 2–11

where the domains of x and y are the set of all real numbers, is obtained as follows. The truth set of "$x < y$" is the set of all ordered pairs of real numbers for which the first number is less than the second; the truth set of "$y < 1$" is the set of all ordered pairs for which the second number is less than 1. In Fig. 2–11 the graphs of the separate sentences are shown with different shadings, and the graph of the conjunction "$x < y$ and $y < 1$" is shown with double shading. (The shadings terminate at the edges of the figure because of space limitations, not because the graphs terminate there.)

The following ideas play a prominent role in school algebra:

(1) Solving an equation in one variable is nothing more than determining the truth set of the open sentence. The solution depends on the set of numbers in the domain of the variable—for certain domains the solution may be the null set, whereas for other domains its truth set may be nonempty.

(2) Stating a property of an algebraic system is a matter of writing an open sentence which is true for every element of the system. For example, the distributive property of the system of real numbers can be stated as:

> For any real number x and any real number y and any real number z, the sentence
> $$x(y + z) = xy + xz$$
> is true.

We usually abbreviate this statement to:

> For any real x, y, z,
> $$x(y + z) = xy + xz.$$

As another example, let A be a variable whose domain is the set of all sentences. Then the law of the excluded middle of logic can be stated as follows.

> For every A, the sentence
>
> $$A \quad \text{or} \quad \text{not-}A$$
>
> is true.

And the law of contradiction is:

> For every A, the sentence
>
> $$A \quad \text{and} \quad \text{not-}A$$
>
> is false.

EXERCISE GROUP 2–2

1. If T denotes "true" and F "false," fill in the following tables with T or F, if possible, where A, B, and C are sentences.

(a)

A	B	A and B	A or B	not-A	if A, then B	not-A or B
T	T					
F	T					
T	F					
F	F					

(b)

A	B	A and not-B	if not-A, then B	if B, then A
T	T			
T	F			
F	T			
F	F			

(c)

A	B	if A, then B	A or B	A and B	A and not-A
		F			
T			F		
				T	
	F	T			

(d)

A	B	not-(A or B)	not-A or not-B	not-(A and B)	not-A and not-B
T	T				
F	F				
T	F				
F	T				

(e)

A	B	C	(A or B) and C	A or (B and C)	(not-A and B) or not-C
T	T	T			
T	T	F			
T	F	T			
T	F	F			
F	F	F			
F	F	T			
F	T	F			
F	T	T			

2. Let the domain of t be the set of positive integers. Then find the truth set of each of the following sentences:

(a) $8 + t < 12$ or $5 + 1 \neq 6$
(b) $8 + t < 12$ or $5 + 1 = 6$
(c) $8 + t < 12$ and $5 + 1 \neq 6$
(d) if $8 + t < 12$, then $5 + 1 = 6$
(e) if $5 + 1 \neq 6$, then $8 + t < 12$
(f) if $8 + t < 12$, then $5 + 1 \neq 6$
(g) $t + 2 = 4$ or $t + 2 \neq 4$
(h) $t + 2 \leq 4$ and $t + 3 > 4$
(i) $(t + 2 < 4$ or $t + 2 < 5)$ and $t + 2 > 3$
(j) $t + 2 < 4$ or $(t + 2 < 5$ and $t + 2 > 3)$
(k) $(t + 2 < 4$ or $t + 2 < 5)$ or $t + 2 > 3$
(l) $t + 2 < 4$ or $(t + 2 < 5$ or $t + 2 > 3)$

3. Let the domain of t be the set of real numbers. Then draw the graph of each sentence in problem 2.

4. Find the truth set of each of the following sentences, where x is the first variable, for the indicated domain R of x and y.

(a) $x = y^2$, $R = \{1, 2, 3, \ldots, 36\}$
(b) $x + 2 = y$ and $x + y = 4$, $R = \{1, 2, 3, \ldots\}$

(c) $x + y = 5$ or $2x + y = 6$, $R = \{1, 2, 3, \ldots\}$
(d) $x + y = 5$ and $2x + y = 6$, $R =$ set of all real numbers
(e) $x < 3$ and $y > 1$, $R = \{1, 2, 3, 4, 5\}$
(f) $x + 2y > 0$ and $2x + y < 0$, $R =$ set of all integers between -4 and 4

5. Draw the graphs of the following sentences for the indicated domain R of each of the variables (consider x as the first variable).

(a) $x + y = 3$ and $2x + y = 5$, $R =$ set of all real numbers
(b) $x + y = 3$ or $2x + y = 5$, $R =$ set of all real numbers
(c) $1 < x^2 + y^2 \leq 4$, $R =$ set of all real numbers
(d) $x < 3$ or $y > 1$, $R =$ set of all real numbers
(e) $2x > y$ and $x < 1$, $R =$ set of all real numbers
(f) $x < y$ and $x < -y$, $R =$ set of all real numbers

2-3. LOGIC OF SENTENCES

In Chapter 3 we shall prove the following property of real numbers:

For any real numbers a and b, $ab > 0$ if and only if ($a > 0$ and $b > 0$) or ($a < 0$ and $b < 0$).

How do we know that this sentence is true for any two real numbers a and b? Is this a rule laid down arbitrarily by mathematicians, or did this property arise through experience with numbers by trial and error?

It happens that this property can be *proved* as a consequence of other more fundamental properties; that is, it is a *theorem*. But what about the other properties from which it is deduced? Are they also theorems? This line of questioning would eventually lead us back to a certain basic set of properties of real numbers. No property included in this basic set of properties could then be deduced from the other properties in this set. We are thus left with a set of properties that cannot be proved.

The words and symbols used in the above property need to be defined. What does the symbol "$<$" mean? When we define its meaning in terms of other words and symbols, we will again be compelled to use a set of words and symbols, none of which can be defined in terms of the others (unless we are tempted to define these basic words in terms of words already defined—a circular type of definition which is mathematically taboo).

Thus we must begin a study of any mathematical system with a set of *undefined* words and symbols. Although no attempt is made to define these words formally, we always have in mind one or more representations of the words. In a study of plane geometry, for example, we begin with undefined words such as "point," "line," "on," "equal," etc., but we may visualize "point" as a spot of ink on a paper, "line" as a streak of ink, etc. In algebra we can begin with the undefined words "number," "sum," "product," "equal," "less than," and symbols representing these words. It is possible to think of many kinds of "numbers" and sums and products of numbers as representations or models of these words, but any logical deduction from these words must be independent of the particular interpretations that might be attached to them.

It should be understood that the choice of words which are left undefined is somewhat arbitrary and is determined partly by convenience (or convention) and by the amount of rigor demanded. It may be possible to select a smaller set of words, or even a different set. Then the others are defined in terms of this set.

Having decided upon a basic set of undefined words, we next agree upon certain properties with which we shall assume these words to comply. These properties are stated in the forms of open sentences, and they impose conditions upon the undefined words; that is, we do not define the words but we assume that they satisfy certain conditions. We call these assumptions *axioms*. They are not "self-evident" or obvious. They are properties which are *assumed* to be true. The axioms chosen are often suggested by our experience with the model we had in mind for the undefined words. In the case of the system of real numbers, as we shall see, the axioms describe the behavior of the two binary operations of the system. We must, however, regard the axioms as independent of any empirical considerations. In this way we hope, by deduction, to make discoveries without explicit experience and then to use these new facts as a check on our experience, and vice versa.

After we select a set of axioms, that is, a set of properties with which our set of undefined terms is assumed to comply, we may then prove *theorems*. These are sentences which can be proved true in accordance with the laws of logical deduction on the basis of the accepted axioms. In this manner we build a body of knowledge about a mathematical system. In summary, we first assume a set of *axioms* to be true with respect to the elements and operations of a system. We next prove that if the axioms are true, certain *theorems* are true. We then prove that if these theorems and the axioms are true, certain other theorems are true, etc. From time to time in the process, we *define* certain new words and symbols in terms of the basic set of undefined words and symbols, and then other words in terms of these words, etc. At no point in the process may we use any information other than that obtained in a prior theorem, a prior definition, or the axioms.

Thus, all the procedures and rules of an algebra can be stated as theorems which can be derived from a basic set of axioms. We shall list the axioms for the algebra of real numbers in Chapter 3.

At this point an objection might be raised. Why can't we avoid all this bother and simply view all the results in school algebra as rules without worrying about which must be proved and which can be assumed? In fact, why prove results that seem obvious anyway?

There is danger in accepting rules without proof. How can the validity of a given rule be tested? We cannot check its truth for *every* value of the variables. If the rules are not derived from some basic set of rules, we will never be sure that they are *consistent* with one another. We say that two statements are *inconsistent* if they contradict each other; that is, if they lead to a statement of the form "A and not-A." As noted earlier, such a statement is false for every sentence A.

Note that it is usually easy to prove the inconsistency of a set of statements; the existence of one counterexample, a specific contradiction, is enough. But proving consistency is another matter. Regardless of how diligently one searches for counterexamples, the mere fact that none is found does not guarantee consistency. After the search is called off, the very next example might have yielded a counterexample. The only way to guarantee consistency of a set of statements is to prove that they are logical consequences of a set of consistent statements, namely, a set of consistent axioms.*

Now that we have discussed the need for proving the results of algebra, the question remains: what do we mean by a "proof"? Too often a result is considered proved if it is "believed," or if it is plausible, or if it is known to be true in a few cases. Having faith in a statement is not enough. In the latter category is the so-called "proof by induction:† "It has been observed that the result has held true in n trials in the past; hence, it will continue to hold true in all cases."

We need not belabor the fact that this is not a proof. Of course, by induction one may arrive at a conjecture which can then be proved by deductive methods. In a fascinating set of books on this subject, *Mathematics and Plausible Reasoning*,‡ G. Polya investigates how one discovers what statements are worth trying to prove and what suggests such statements in the first place.

In algebra, theorems are written as conditional compound sentences of the form

$$\text{if} \quad p, \quad \text{then} \quad q,$$

where p and q are open sentences. Thus, we mean by "the proof of a theorem" the process of showing that a conditional sentence is true *for all values of the variables*. (Let us call such a conditional *true*, for short.)

---

* The problem of proving that a given set of axioms is consistent is a fundamental and difficult job not to be tackled here.

† Not to be confused with *mathematical induction*, which is a powerful and valid method of proving special types of statements. (See Section 4–1.)

‡ Princeton University Press, 1954.

The sentence p is called the *hypothesis*. The sentence q is the *conclusion*. There are several methods of proof available.

Direct Proof. A basic principle of logic is the *law of transitivity of conditionals*.

If the conditionals (if A, then B) and (if B, then C) are true, then the conditional (if A, then C) is true.

This law can be stated more compactly by writing the true conditional, "if A, then B" (read "A *implies* B") as

$$A \Rightarrow B.$$

(A true conditional is often called an *implication*.) Then the law is written as

$$(A \Rightarrow B \quad \text{and} \quad B \Rightarrow C) \Rightarrow (A \Rightarrow C),$$

and the transitivity of the implications becomes more apparent.

A direct proof of the theorem "$p \Rightarrow q$" is usually effected by collecting known axioms and theorems in the following format:

$$p \Rightarrow r, \quad r \Rightarrow s, \quad s \Rightarrow t, \ldots, \quad u \Rightarrow q.$$

Then, by transitivity, $p \Rightarrow q$.

For example, consider the theorem: If $a = b$, then $a - b = 0$. Here, we must prove "$p \Rightarrow q$," where p is the sentence "$a = b$" and q is the sentence "$a - b = 0$." Let us assume that it has been established previously that

$$a = b \Rightarrow a + (-b) = b + (-b)$$

and

$$a + (-b) = b + (-b) \Rightarrow a - b = 0.$$

Then, by transitivity,

$$a = b \Rightarrow a - b = 0.$$

In passing, we should note the many forms, all of which are equivalent, in which the implication is written in mathematics. (Two open sentences are equivalent if their truth sets are equal.)

(if p, then q) is true;

$p \Rightarrow q$;

q if p;

p only if q;

q is a necessary condition for p;

p is a sufficient condition for q;

not-$q \Rightarrow$ not-p.

The last of these forms is called the *contrapositive* of the implication. We may take the view that each of the above forms is a restatement of the implication "$p \Rightarrow q$" and that any one statement may be replaced by any other in a mathematical argument. Thus, if one of the sentences above is proved, then all the others are also proved.

As was mentioned before, the sentence "p if and only if q" is really a statement of the conjunction of two conditionals:

$$\text{(if } p, \text{ then } q) \qquad \text{and} \qquad \text{(if } q, \text{ then } p).$$

Thus, to prove a theorem of the form "p if and only if q," we must really prove two theorems:

$$p \Rightarrow q \qquad \text{and} \qquad q \Rightarrow p.$$

Indirect Proof. This method is often called *proof by contradiction*. By "contradiction" we mean a sentence of the form

$$\text{"}A \qquad \text{and} \qquad \text{not-}A.\text{"}$$

We assumed earlier (the law of contradiction) that such a sentence is always false for any sentence A.

Example. Let us give an indirect proof of the theorem:

If a is an integer and a^2 is divisible by 2, then a is divisible by 2.

An indirect proof consists of assuming that the theorem is not true and showing that this assumption leads to a contradiction. If we assume that the theorem of our example is not true, we are assuming that

a^2 is divisible by 2 and a is not divisible by 2.

If we can show that this assumption leads to a contradiction, we can argue that our assumption must be false; that is, the theorem must be true.

The assumption may be rephrased as:

$a^2 = 2c$ for some integer c and $a = 2d + 1$ for some integer d.

If $a = 2d + 1$, then by squaring we have

$$a^2 = 4d^2 + 4d + 1 = 2(2d^2 + 2d) + 1.$$

Now

$a^2 = 2c$ and $a = 2d + 1 \Rightarrow$

$$a^2 = 2c \text{ and } a^2 = 2(2d^2 + 2d) + 1.$$

But the sentence,

$$a^2 = 2c \qquad \text{and} \qquad a^2 = 2(2d^2 + 2d) + 1$$

is a contradiction because a^2 cannot be twice an integer c and at the same time one more than twice an integer $(2d^2 + 2d)$. Hence our assumption leads to a contradiction, and we are forced to conclude that the assumption is false. But since our assumption was that the theorem is false, the theorem is true.

The method of indirect proof consists of proving "$p \Rightarrow q$" by proving that "p and not q" implies a contradiction; that is,

$$(p \text{ and not } q) \Rightarrow r,$$

where r is a contradiction.

REMARK: Let us examine the implication

$$(p \text{ and not-}q) \Rightarrow r,$$

which appears in an indirect proof of "$p \Rightarrow q$." Since r is a contradiction, it is false. Therefore, "p and not-q" must also be false; otherwise, the statement could not be a true conditional. (Recall the definition of a true conditional.) Finally, we note that

"p and not-q"   is equivalent to   "not-(if p, then q)."

[See problem 1(h).] Since "p and not-q" is false, we conclude that "if p, then q" is true.

There is no general rule which tells us how to arrive at a contradiction. This comes only with experience. Nevertheless, the indirect method often provides an attack on an "obvious" theorem which eludes the direct method. This is particularly true when the theorem is a statement about *all* the elements of a set; then, an indirect proof starts with an assumption that *some* elements are *not* in the set.

Since the statement "not-$q \Rightarrow$ not-p" is equivalent to "$p \Rightarrow q$", there exists another indirect method of proof which consists of proving the contrapositive of the theorem. Thus, in the preceding example, another indirect proof would be obtained by proving the contrapositive, namely,

"If the integer a is not divisible by 2, then a^2 is not divisible by 2."

A pertinent question at this point is: How much of algebra should be proved in a first course? A considered opinion is that the student should be asked to prove very few theorems but should be exposed to enough proofs in various degrees of completeness to enable him to understand methods and the necessity of proof and the satisfaction of devising and understanding theorems. The student should become convinced that it is preferable to work with results that are to be proved rather than merely accepted as rules, even though he is not mature enough to carry out such a program in detail. He should be made to realize that one *could* prove the various properties as consequences of basic properties. He must always be told the truth about a result—that it is being accepted temporarily without proof, but that it can be proved. Occasionally the outlines of proofs can be carried out until the student acquires a feeling for the meaning of proof. By the end of the course, the more able students should be ready for a discussion of the axiomatic basis of algebra.

The teacher, for his part, should have from the very beginning of the course, a clear idea of precisely what assumptions underlie the algebra being taught. Although developing all the results of algebra from the axioms is a long, exacting task, the teacher should be familiar enough with this development to understand its framework and methodology. Portions of Chapters 3, 4, and 5 will be devoted to this development.

EXERCISE GROUP 2-3

1. Two compound open sentences are *equivalent* if their truth sets are equal, provided their variables have the same domain. Equivalence can sometimes be shown by means of truth tables. For example, consider the open sentences

$$\text{``if} \quad A, \quad \text{then} \quad B\text{''}$$

and

$$\text{``if} \quad \text{not-}B, \quad \text{then} \quad \text{not-}A\text{''}$$

(called *contrapositives*), where A and B are open sentences. For any common value of the variables, there are certain possible cases of A, B true or false; for each case we determine the truth of the compound sentences as follows.

A	B	if A, then B	not-B	not-A	if not-B, then not-A
T	T	T	F	F	T
F	T	T	F	T	T
T	F	F	T	F	F
F	F	T	T	T	T

Since the truth tables for the two compound open sentences are the same in every case, we have shown that the sentences are equivalent. In symbolic form,

$$(A \Rightarrow B) \Leftrightarrow (\text{not-}B \Rightarrow \text{not-}A).$$

By means of truth tables, decide which of the following pairs of open sentences are equivalent.

(a) If A, then B; not-A or B

(b) A or not-B; not-A and B

(c) If A, then B; if B, then A. (These sentences are *converses*.)

(d) If A, then B; if not-A, then not-B. (These sentences are *inverses*.)

(e) Not-(A and B); not-A or not-B

(f) Not-(A or B); not-A and not-B

(g) Not-(if A, then B); if A, then not-B

(h) Not-(if A, then B); A and not-B

2. Write in symbolic form the facts about pairs of equivalent sentences learned in problem 1. In particular, what is the negative of a conjunction? of a disjunction? of a conditional? Use these results to write the contrapositive of:

(a) If (A or B), then C

(b) If A, then (B and C)

(c) If (if A, then B), then (C or D)

(d) If (A or not-B), then not-(C or D)

3. Find counterexamples to disprove the statements below.

(a) If x is a real number, then $\sqrt{x^2} + 1 = x + 1$.

(b) If x is a real number, then $3x^2 + 4 = 4 - 2x + 5x^2$.

(c) If n is a positive integer, then $n^2 - n + 41$ is a prime.

(d) If x is a real number, then $\sqrt{x^2} = x$.

(e) If x is a real number, then

$$\frac{x^2 - 1}{x - 1} = x + 1.$$

(f) If x is a real number, then

$$\frac{x}{x} = 1.$$

(g) If x and y are nonnegative real numbers, then

$$x + y > 2\sqrt{xy}.$$

4. Decide which type of proof is best suited for each of the following theorems. Then prove the theorems.

(a) If the integer a is divisible by 2, then a^2 is divisible by 2.

(b) If a is an integer and a^3 is divisible by 2, then a is divisible by 2.

(c) If b is a prime and b is greater than 2, then b is not divisible by 2.

Chapter 3

Structure of an Ordered Field

3-1. THE REAL NUMBERS: MODEL OF AN ORDERED FIELD

Much of elementary algebra is concerned with the system of real numbers. How does the mathematician study a specific model such as the real numbers? He forms an abstract system of undefined elements and operations and assumes that this abstract system obeys the properties that the model is known to possess. Then he studies the abstract system; in this way he may discover structural properties that he did not notice in the model.

We shall form an abstract system called a *complete ordered field*. Its elements and operations will be left undefined, and its axioms will be suggested by our knowledge of familiar operations on real numbers. For convenience, let us call the undefined elements "numbers," remembering that this is merely a name.

Our abstract system then consists of a set $\mathfrak{F}$ of undefined elements symbolized by $a, b, c, \ldots, 0, 1$ with two undefined binary operations (called *addition* and *multiplication*, symbolized by $+$ and $\cdot$). The symbol $=$ represents an equivalence in $\mathfrak{F}$ and is used to assert the fact that two particular symbols represent the same element of $\mathfrak{F}$.

The basic properties, or *axioms*, which characterize the operations of the system $(\mathfrak{F}, +, \cdot)$ are listed in three groups. The first group consists of the *field axioms*; any system with two operations which satisfies these axioms is called a *field*. Next are the *order axioms*, which endow the elements of $\mathfrak{F}$ with relative size. Finally, the *completeness axiom* guarantees that there are enough elements in the system so that it will have all the properties of the real number model. The completeness axiom and its implications will be dealt with in Chapter 5.

3-2. AXIOMS FOR A FIELD

Let us assume that for any elements a and b in $\mathfrak{F}$, there is a unique element $a + b$ and a unique element $a \cdot b$ in $\mathfrak{F}$ such that the following are true:

F1. For any a and b in $\mathfrak{F}$,

$$a + b = b + a \quad \text{and} \quad a \cdot b = b \cdot a.$$

F2. For any a, b, and c in $\mathfrak{F}$,

$$(a + b) + c = a + (b + c) \qquad \text{and} \qquad (a \cdot b) \cdot c = a \cdot (b \cdot c).$$

F3. For any a, b, and c in $\mathfrak{F}$,

$$a \cdot (b + c) = (a \cdot b) + (a \cdot c).$$

F4. There is an element in $\mathfrak{F}$, denoted by "0," such that

$$a + 0 = 0 + a = a$$

for every a in $\mathfrak{F}$.

F5. There is an element in $\mathfrak{F}$, denoted by "1," different from 0, such that

$$a \cdot 1 = 1 \cdot a = a$$

for every a in $\mathfrak{F}$.

F6. For each a in $\mathfrak{F}$ there is an element in $\mathfrak{F}$ denoted by "$-a$" such that

$$a + (-a) = (-a) + a = 0.$$

($-a$ is called the *additive inverse* of a.)

F7. For each a in $\mathfrak{F}$ except 0 there is an element in $\mathfrak{F}$ denoted by "$1/a$" such that

$$a \cdot \frac{1}{a} = \frac{1}{a} \cdot a = 1.$$

($1/a$ is called the *multiplicative inverse* of a.)

The field axioms include the familiar axioms for a group. In fact, a field is a commutative group with respect to its first operation (addition), and if we delete the identity for addition, the remaining elements form a commutative group with respect to the second operation (multiplication). The two operations of a field are linked by the distributive property.

For convenience we shall omit the operation symbol $\cdot$ whenever confusion will not result and write "ab" for "$a \cdot b$." Let us agree also that multiplication shall be performed before addition, except where indicated otherwise; this convention will allow us to minimize the use of parentheses. For example, we may write the distributive property as

$$a(b + c) = ab + ac.$$

We are using the symbol "0," *zero*, as the identity for addition and the symbol "1," *one*, as the identity for multiplication. It must be remembered that these are only symbols, and any other symbols or names could have been chosen. The same is true of the symbols "$+$" and "$\cdot$." We must avoid the temptation to endow these symbols with meanings that are intuitively associated with them; their only meanings are provided by the field axioms.

Note the assumption in F5 that $0 \neq 1$. This "obvious" fact does not follow from the other axioms and must be assumed.

Before we begin to deduce new properties of the operations from the field axioms, let us comment on the equivalence "$=$" in the set.

Since "$=$" is an equivalence, it partitions the symbols used for elements of $\mathfrak{F}$ into classes such that for a, b, c in $\mathfrak{F}$,

E1. $a = a$,

E2. $a = b \Rightarrow b = a$,

E3. $a = b$ and $b = c \Rightarrow a = c$.

If two symbols are in the same class, they name one number. We think of that number as being represented by the whole class of symbols.

We make further requirements of $=$ in $\mathfrak{F}$. We require that the operations be *well defined* with respect to $=$; that is, since a given symbol must represent one and only one element of $\mathfrak{F}$, the sum and product of two given elements of $\mathfrak{F}$ do not depend on the choices of symbols for the elements. Formally, this means that

E4. $a = b$ and $c = d \Rightarrow a + c = b + d$,

E5. $a = b$ and $c = d \Rightarrow ac = bd$.

In any description of a mathematical system, we must be careful to require not only an equivalence in the set but also operations that are well defined with respect to the equivalence.

The familiar manipulations of algebra are now *consequences* of F1 through F7. We shall consider a few of these consequences (theorems). Some will be proved, and others, marked with an asterisk (*), will be left as exercises for the reader. As an example of the style of proof to be used, we prove the theorem:

If a, b, and c are any elements of $\mathfrak{F}$, then

$$(a + b) + c = b + (c + a).$$

Proof. We wish to show that the number obtained as the sum of $(a + b)$ and c is the same number that is obtained as the sum of b and $(c + a)$. We know that

$$(a + b) + c = c + (a + b),$$

by applying F1 to $(a + b)$ and c, since $(a + b)$ is in $\mathcal{F}$; also,

$$c + (a + b) = (c + a) + b,$$

by F2. Hence

$$(a + b) + c = (c + a) + b,$$

by the transitive property of equality, E3. We also have

$$(c + a) + b = b + (c + a),$$

by applying F1 to $(c + a)$ and b; hence

$$(a + b) + c = b + (c + a),$$

by E3. This is the desired result.

In subsequent proofs we shall abbreviate the work as shown below:

$$\begin{aligned}
(a + b) + c &= c + (a + b) && \text{F1}\\
&= (c + a) + b && \text{F2}\\
&= b + (c + a), && \text{F1}
\end{aligned}$$

where closure under addition and the transitivity of equality are used without mention.

Let us review some of the properties of fields that we previously proved as group properties. We repeat the proofs to show suggested forms of exposition.

Theorem 3–1   (*Uniqueness of additive inverse*). If a and b are any elements in $\mathcal{F}$ such that

$$a + b = 0, \qquad \text{then} \quad b = -a.$$

Proof. By hypothesis,

$$a + b = 0.$$

Then

$$(-a) + (a + b) = (-a) + 0 \qquad\qquad \text{E4}$$

and

$$[(-a) + a] + b = -a \qquad\qquad \text{F2 and F4}$$

and

$$0 + b = -a \qquad\qquad \text{F6}$$

and

$$b = -a. \qquad\qquad \text{F4}$$

Note that F6 assumes the *existence* of an additive inverse $(-a)$ of a. Then Theorem 3–1 shows that there is only one additive inverse of a, thus proving its *uniqueness*.

Theorem 3–2 (*Cancellation property for addition*). If a, b, and c are any elements in $\mathfrak{F}$ such that $a + b = a + c$, then $b = c$.

Proof. We know that $-a = -a$ and $a + b = a + c$, by hypothesis. Then

$$(-a) + (a + b) = (-a) + (a + c), \qquad \text{E4}$$
$$[(-a) + a] + b = [(-a) + a] + c. \qquad \text{F2}$$

Then

$$0 + b = 0 + c, \qquad \text{F6}$$
$$b = c. \qquad \text{F4}$$

Theorem 3–3. For any a in $\mathfrak{F}$, $a = -(-a)$.

Proof.

$$(-a) + a = 0. \qquad \text{F6}$$

Hence

$$a = -(-a). \qquad \text{Theorem 3–1}$$

Theorem 3–4. For any a and b in $\mathfrak{F}$, $(-a) + (-b) = -(b + a)$.

Proof.
$$(b + a) + [(-a) + (-b)] = [(b + a) + (-a)] + (-b) \qquad \text{F2}$$
$$= \{b + [a + (-a)]\} + (-b) \qquad \text{F2}$$
$$= (b + 0) + (-b) \qquad \text{F6}$$
$$= b + (-b) \qquad \text{F4}$$
$$= 0. \qquad \text{F6}$$

Hence,

$$(-a) + (-b) = -(b + a). \qquad \text{Theorem 3–1}$$

Note that Theorem 3–4 is true in any group. In a field, which is a commutative group with respect to $+$, we may write

$$(-a) + (-b) = -(a + b). \qquad \text{(Why?)}$$

Theorem 3–5. The equation $a + x = b$ has the unique solution $(-a) + b$; that is, there is one, and only one, number x such that $a + x = b$; namely, $x = (-a) + b$.

Proof. First, we verify that if $x = (-a) + b$, then $a + x = b$; that is, we verify that $(-a) + b$ *is* a solution. If $x = (-a) + b$, then

$$a + x = a + [(-a) + b] \qquad \text{E4}$$
$$= [a + (-a)] + b \qquad \text{F2}$$
$$= 0 + b \qquad \text{F6}$$
$$= b. \qquad \text{F4}$$

Next, we show that this solution is unique. Suppose that there are two solutions, x and x'. Then

$$a + x = b \quad \text{and} \quad a + x' = b,$$

and

$$a + x = a + x', \tag{E3}$$
$$x = x'. \tag{Theorem 3–2}$$

Thus, there is only one solution.

In these proofs we see the interesting and powerful way in which we use the uniqueness of the additive inverse.

Each of Theorems 3–1 through 3–5 involves only the operation of addition and can be proved with the axioms of an additive group. Corresponding theorems involving multiplication may be proved with the axioms of a multiplicative group (if the 0 element is deleted). Note the parallel between the following pairs of theorems (a and b any elements in $\mathfrak{F}$):

Theorem 3–1.

$a + b = 0 \Rightarrow b = (-a).$

Theorem 3–1'.

$ab = 1 \quad \text{and} \quad a \neq 0 \Rightarrow b = \dfrac{1}{a}.$

Theorem 3–2.

$a + b = a + c \Rightarrow b = c.$

*Theorem 3–2'.

$ab = ac \quad \text{and} \quad a \neq 0 \Rightarrow b = c.$

Theorem 3–3.

$a = -(-a).$

*Theorem 3–3'.

$a \neq 0 \Rightarrow a = \dfrac{1}{1/a}.$

Theorem 3–4.

$(-a) + (-b) = -(a + b).$

*Theorem 3–4'.

$ab \neq 0 \Rightarrow \left(\dfrac{1}{a}\right)\left(\dfrac{1}{b}\right) = \dfrac{1}{ab}.$

Theorem 3–5.

$a + x = b$ has the unique solution $(-a) + b.$

Theorem 3–5'.

$ax = b,\ a \neq 0,$ has the unique solution $\left(\dfrac{1}{a}\right)b.$

We shall give the proof of Theorem 3–1'; and leave the rest for the reader.

Proof of Theorem 3–1'. If $ab = 1$ and $a \neq 0$, then $1/a$ is in $\mathfrak{F}$ and

$$\left(\frac{1}{a}\right)(ab) = \left(\frac{1}{a}\right) \cdot 1. \tag{E5}$$

On the left,
$$\left(\frac{1}{a}\right)(ab) = \left(\frac{1}{a}\cdot a\right)(b) \qquad \text{F2}$$
$$= 1\cdot b \qquad \text{F7}$$
$$= b. \qquad \text{F5}$$

On the right,
$$\left(\frac{1}{a}\right)(1) = \frac{1}{a}\cdot \qquad \text{F5}$$

Hence,
$$b = \frac{1}{a}\cdot \qquad \text{E3}$$

New properties of a field may be proved which involve both operations of the field.

Theorem 3–6. For any a in $\mathfrak{F}$,
$$a\cdot 0 = 0\cdot a = 0.$$

Proof.
$$a = a \qquad \text{and} \qquad 1 + 0 = 1, \qquad \text{F4}$$
$$a(1 + 0) = a\cdot 1 \qquad \text{E5}$$
$$= a \qquad \text{F5}$$
$$= a + 0. \qquad \text{F4}$$

Also
$$a(1 + 0) = a\cdot 1 + a\cdot 0 \qquad \text{F3}$$
$$= a + a\cdot 0. \qquad \text{F5}$$

Then
$$a + a\cdot 0 = a + 0, \qquad \text{E3}$$
$$a\cdot 0 = 0. \qquad \text{Theorem 3–2}$$

Also
$$0\cdot a = 0. \qquad \text{F1}$$

*Theorem 3–7.** For any a, b and c in $\mathfrak{F}$,
$$(a + b)c = ac + bc.$$

Theorem 3–8. For any a and b in $\mathfrak{F}$,
$$(-a)(b) = -(ab).$$

Proof.
$$ab + (-a)(b) = [a + (-a)]b \qquad \text{Theorem 3–7}$$
$$= 0\cdot b \qquad \text{F6}$$
$$= 0. \qquad \text{Theorem 3–6}$$

Hence,
$$(-a)(b) = -(ab). \qquad \text{Theorem 3–1}$$

*Theorem 3–9. For any a and b in $\mathfrak{F}$,

$$(-a)(-b) = ab.$$

*Theorem 3–10. For any a in $\mathfrak{F}$,

$$(-1) \cdot a = -a.$$

New operations on elements of a field are now defined in terms of addition and multiplication.

Definition. For any a and b in $\mathfrak{F}$,

(1) the number $a - b$, called "the result of *subtracting* b from a" or "the *difference* of a and b," is defined as

$$a - b = a + (-b);$$

(2) the number

$$\frac{a}{b}, \qquad b \neq 0,$$

called "the result of *dividing* a by b" or "the *quotient* of a and b," is defined as

$$\frac{a}{b} = a \cdot \left(\frac{1}{b}\right).$$

The difference $a - b$ is unique because it is defined as the sum of a and $(-b)$, which is a unique sum. The quotient

$$\frac{a}{b}, \qquad b \neq 0,$$

is unique because it is the product of a and $1/b$, which is a unique product.

Here we can quickly clear up the question of division by zero. By Theorem 3–5' the equation $ax = b$ has the unique solution $\left(\dfrac{1}{a}\right)b$, which by definition is b/a. Now let $b = 1$ and $a = 0$ so that

$$\frac{b}{a} = \frac{1}{0}.$$

Assume that $1/0$ is the solution of $0x = 1$. But by Theorem 3–6, $0x = 0$ for every x in $\mathfrak{F}$. Now $0x = 1$ and $0x = 0$ imply $1 = 0$, a contradiction. Hence, the equation $0x = 1$ has *no* solution. Thus, $1/0$ is not a symbol for any element in $\mathfrak{F}$, and a similar argument shows that $b/0$ is not uniquely defined for any b in $\mathfrak{F}$. In other words, we have shown that zero *has no reciprocal* in $\mathfrak{F}$. In our subsequent development, we shall always assume that for an element of the form a/b, $b \neq 0$.

Among the many theorems that can be proved, we choose as examples the following:

*Theorem 3–11.

$$(b - a) + a = b.$$

*Theorem 3–11′.

$$\left(\frac{b}{a}\right) a = b.$$

*Theorem 3–12.

$$a - (b + c) = (a - b) - c.$$

*Theorem 3–12′.

$$\frac{a}{bc} = \left(\frac{a}{b}\right)\left(\frac{1}{c}\right).$$

Theorem 3–13. $a(b - c) = ab - ac.$

Proof. Since $a = a$ and $b - c = b + (-c)$,

$$
\begin{aligned}
a(b - c) &= a[b + (-c)] & \text{E5} \\
&= ab + a(-c) & \text{F3} \\
&= ab + [-(ac)] & \text{Theorem 3–8} \\
&= ab - ac.
\end{aligned}
$$

*Theorem 3–14. If $ab = 0$, then $a = 0$ or $b = 0$. (Do not confuse with the converse, "If $a = 0$ or $b = 0$, then $ab = 0$," which is a restatement of Theorem 3–6.)

*Theorem 3–15.

$$a - b = c - d$$

if and only if

$$a + d = b + c.$$

*Theorem 3–15′.

$$\frac{a}{b} = \frac{c}{d}$$

if and only if

$$ad = bc \quad \text{and} \quad bd \neq 0.$$

*Theorem 3–16.

$$(a - b) + (c - d) = (a + c) - (b + d).$$

*Theorem 3–16′.

$$\left(\frac{a}{b}\right)\left(\frac{c}{d}\right) = \frac{ac}{bd}, \quad bd \neq 0.$$

Theorem 3–17. $\dfrac{ab}{cb} = \dfrac{a}{c}, \quad cb \neq 0.$

Proof.

$$
\begin{aligned}
(ab)c &= a(bc) & \text{F2} \\
&= (bc)a & \text{F1} \\
&= (cb)a. & \text{F1}
\end{aligned}
$$

Since

$$(ab)c = (cb)a \quad \text{and} \quad cb \neq 0,$$

$$\frac{ab}{cb} = \frac{a}{c}. \qquad \text{Theorem 3–15′}$$

Theorem 3-18.

$$\frac{a}{b} + \frac{c}{d} = \frac{ad + bc}{bd}, \qquad bd \neq 0.$$

Proof.

$$\frac{a}{b} = \frac{ad}{bd} \quad \text{and} \quad \frac{c}{d} = \frac{bc}{bd}, \qquad \text{Theorem 3–17, F1}$$

$$\frac{a}{b} + \frac{c}{d} = \frac{ad}{bd} + \frac{bc}{bd}, \qquad \text{E4}$$

$$= ad\left(\frac{1}{bd}\right) + bc\left(\frac{1}{bd}\right) \qquad \text{Definition}$$

$$= (ad + bc)\left(\frac{1}{bd}\right) \qquad \text{Theorem 3–7}$$

$$= \frac{ad + bc}{bd}. \qquad \text{Definition}$$

*Theorem 3–19.

$$\frac{\dfrac{a}{b}}{\dfrac{c}{d}} = \frac{ad}{bc}, \qquad b \neq 0, \quad c \neq 0, \quad d \neq 0.$$

EXERCISE GROUP 3–2

If a, b, c, and d are in $\mathfrak{F}$, prove the statements of problems 1 through 7.

1. $(-b) + (a + b) = a$
2. $(1/b)(ab) = a, b \neq 0$
3. $(-1) + b(a + 1/b) = ab, b \neq 0$
4. If $a = b$, then $-a = -b$.
5. $-0 = 0$.
6. If $a = b$ and $c = d$, then $a - c = b - d$.
7. $a - (-b) = a + b$
8. Solve the equation: $x + a = b + c$ for x; a, b, c, x in $\mathfrak{F}$.
9. Solve the equation: $(x - 1)/(x + 1) = 0$ for x a real number.

10. Is the binary operation of subtraction commutative? associative? If not, give counterexamples.

11. Under ordinary addition and multiplication, which of the following sets are fields? If they are not, what is lacking?

(a) The set of integers
(b) The set of numbers $b\sqrt{2}$, where b is any rational number
(c) The set of numbers $a + b\sqrt{2}$, where a and b are any rational numbers

12. Consider the set of integers $\{0, 1, 2, 3, 4\}$ obtained as remainders after dividing any integers by 5. Define the sum $a + b$ and the product ab of two elements of this set as the remainders after dividing the usual sum and product by 5. Thus, $3 + 4 = 2$, $4 \cdot 4 = 1$, etc. Decide whether this set and these two

operations are a field. If so, what is the additive inverse of 3? the multiplicative inverse of 3?

13. Follow the instructions in problem 12, but use the integers $\{0, 1, 2, 3, 4, 5\}$ and divide by 6.

14. Verify that the set $\{E, O\}$ and the operations $+$ and $\times$ as defined in problem 1 of Exercise Group 1-3 form a field.

15. Prove that in a field the identities for addition and multiplication are unique.

16. Prove that zero is the only real number with the property that $0 = -0$.

17. Verify that a set $\mathfrak{F}$ of elements with binary operations $+$ and $\cdot$ is a *field* if

(a) $(\mathfrak{F}, +, \cdot)$ is a commutative ring
(b) there is an identity 1 (different from 0) for $\cdot$, and
(c) for each nonzero element a of $\mathfrak{F}$, there is an element $1/a$ of $\mathfrak{F}$ such that

$$a \cdot \frac{1}{a} = 1.$$

3-3. AXIOMS FOR AN ORDERED FIELD

A second, additional set of axioms will be assumed for the elements of $\mathfrak{F}$. These will impose an order on the elements of $\mathfrak{F}$. A field which satisfies the following axioms will be called an *ordered field*.

In addition to the relation of equality, we introduce a new relation denoted by the symbol "$<$." The statement "$a < b$" is read as "a is *less than b*." We assume now that the system $(\mathfrak{F}, +, \cdot)$, in addition to being a field, has an order relation $<$ and satisfies the following axioms.

Order axioms

O1. If a and b are any elements in $\mathfrak{F}$, then *one, and only one,* of the following is true:

$$a = b, \quad a < b, \quad b < a.$$

O2. If a, b, c are any elements in $\mathfrak{F}$ such that $a < b$ and $b < c$, then

$$a < c.$$

O3. If a, b, c are any elements in $\mathfrak{F}$ such that $a < b$, then

$$a + c < b + c.$$

O4. If a, b, c are any elements in $\mathfrak{F}$ such that $a < b$ and $0 < c$, then

$$ac < bc.$$

As a matter of notation, we agree that "$a < b$" and "$b > a$" are the same statement, where the latter is read "b is *greater than a*." Thus, the order axioms may be rephrased in terms of the symbol "$>$." We also recall that

$$a \leq b \qquad \text{means} \qquad a < b \quad \text{or} \quad a = b$$

and

$$a \not< b \qquad \text{means} \qquad a \text{ is } not \text{ less than } b.$$

In the light of O1,

$$a \not< b \qquad \text{means} \qquad a = b \quad \text{or} \quad b < a$$

and

$$a \not\leq b \qquad \text{means} \qquad b < a.$$

We say that a is *positive* when $0 < a$ and that a is *negative* when $a < 0$.

Note that the truth of "$a < b$" is not altered when we use different symbols to represent a and b. This fact can be stated formally as

E6.   If $a = c$, $b = d$, and $a < b$, then $c < d$.

Some consequences of the order axioms are stated in the following theorems:

Theorem 3–20.   For any a and b in $\mathfrak{F}$,

$$a < b \qquad \text{if and only if} \qquad 0 < b - a;$$

that is, "a is less than b" means that "$b - a$ is positive."

Proof of "$a < b \Rightarrow 0 < b - a$"

$a < b,$	Hypothesis
$a + (-a) < b + (-a),$	O3
$0 < b - a.$	Definition, F6

Proof of "$a < b \Leftarrow 0 < b - a$"

$0 < b - a,$	Hypothesis
$0 + a < (b - a) + a,$	O3
$0 + a < b + [(-a) + a],$	Definition, F2
$a < b.$	F6, F4

*Corollaries to Theorem 3–20.

(1) $a > b$ if and only if $a - b > 0.$
(2) $b < 0$ if and only if $0 < -b.$
(3) $b > 0$ if and only if $0 > -b.$

By means of O1 we can sort all real numbers into three disjoint subsets:

(1) The set P of all positive real numbers.

(2) $\{0\}$.

(3) The set N of all negative real numbers.

Hence, given any element in $\mathfrak{F}$, it belongs to one, and only one, of the sets P, $\{0\}$, N.

By virtue of O2 through O4 we are assured that if both a and b are positive, then so are $a + b$ and ab. If one is positive and the other is negative, then their product is negative. If both a and b are negative, then $a + b$ is negative and ab is positive. Stated formally, we have

Theorem 3–21. If $a > 0$ and $b > 0$, then

$$a + b > 0 \qquad \text{and} \qquad ab > 0.$$

Proof.	$a > 0 \qquad$ and $\qquad b = b,$	Hypothesis
	$a + b > 0 + b,$	O3
	$a + b > b,$	F4
	$b > 0,$	Hypothesis
	$a + b > 0.$	O2

Also, if $a > 0$ and $b > 0$, then

$ab > 0 \cdot b,$	O4
$ab > 0.$	Theorem 3–6

*Corollary to Theorem 3–21. If $ab > 0$ and $a > 0$, then $b > 0$.

*Theorem 3–22. If $a > 0$ and $b < 0$, then $ab < 0$.

*Theorem 3–23. If $a < 0$ and $b < 0$, then

$$a + b < 0 \qquad \text{and} \qquad ab > 0.$$

*Corollary to Theorem 3–23. If $ab > 0$ and $a < 0$, then $b < 0$.

Theorem 3–24. If $a + c < b + c$, then $a < b$.

Proof.	$a + c < b + c,$	Hypothesis
	$0 < (b + c) - (a + c),$	Theorem 3–20
	$(b + c) - (a + c) = b - a,$	(Why?)
	$0 < b - a,$	E6
	$a < b.$	Theorem 3–20

Note that Theorem 3–24 is the converse of O3.

Theorem 3–25. If $ac < bc$ and $c > 0$, then $a < b$.

Note the relation between Theorem 3–25 and O4.

Theorem 3–26. For $c < 0$,

$$a < b \quad \text{if and only if} \quad ac > bc.$$

Theorem 3–27. If $a \neq 0$, then $a^2 > 0$.

It was assumed in F5 that $1 \neq 0$. Hence, by O1, $0 > 1$ or $1 > 0$. Now we can use Theorem 3–27 to prove

Theorem 3–28. $1 > 0$.

Proof.

$1 \neq 0$,	F5
$1^2 > 0$,	Theorem 3–27
$1^2 = 1$,	F5
$1 > 0$.	E6

Theorem 3–29.

$$ab > 0 \Leftrightarrow (a > 0 \text{ and } b > 0) \text{ or } (a < 0 \text{ and } b < 0).$$

Proof of $\Rightarrow$: $ab > 0$, *by hypothesis.* If either a or b is zero, then $ab = 0$, which is contrary to hypothesis. Hence, neither a nor b is zero. If either a or b is positive, say $a > 0$, then $ab > 0$, $a > 0$, implies $b > 0$, by the corollary to Theorem 3–21. Hence, if either a or b is positive, the other is also positive. Finally, if either a or b is negative, say $a < 0$, then $ab > 0$, $a < 0$, implies $b < 0$, by the corollary to Theorem 3–23. Thus, if either a or b is negative, the other is also negative.

Proof of $\Leftarrow$. This follows immediately from Theorems 3–21 and 3–23.

Theorem 3–30.

$$ab < 0 \Leftrightarrow (a > 0 \text{ and } b < 0) \text{ or } (a < 0 \text{ and } b > 0).$$

Theorem 3–31.

$$\frac{1}{b} > 0 \Leftrightarrow b > 0.$$

Corollary to Theorem 3–31.

$$\frac{a}{b} > 0 \Leftrightarrow ab > 0.$$

The order axioms and the consequent theorems form a basis for the solutions of inequalities. We shall illustrate this with several examples in the real number system (which is an ordered field).

Example 1. Find the truth set of $2x + 4 < 5x + 3$, x a real number.

We know that

$$a < b \Leftrightarrow a + c < b + c$$

by O3 and Theorem 3–24. Hence

$$2x + 4 < 5x + 3 \Leftrightarrow -3x < -1$$

by adding $-5x - 4$ to both sides of the inequality. This means that "$2x + 4 < 5x + 3$" and "$-3x < -1$" have the same truth set. We also know from Theorem 3–26 that for $c < 0$,

$$a < b \Leftrightarrow ac > bc.$$

Then

$$-3x < -1 \Leftrightarrow x > \tfrac{1}{3}$$

by multiplying by $(-\tfrac{1}{3})$. By transitivity of inequalities, O2, the sentences "$2x + 4 < 5x + 3$" and "$x > \tfrac{1}{3}$" have exactly the same truth set. Hence, the truth set is the set of all real numbers greater than $\tfrac{1}{3}$.

Example 2. Solve $(x - 3)(2 - 3x) > 0$, x a real number.
By Theorem 3–29,

$$(x - 3)(2 - 3x) > 0 \Leftrightarrow (x - 3 > 0 \text{ and } 2 - 3x > 0)$$
$$\text{or } (x - 3 < 0 \text{ and } 2 - 3x < 0)$$
$$\Leftrightarrow (x > 3 \text{ and } x < \tfrac{2}{3}) \text{ or } (x < 3 \text{ and } x > \tfrac{2}{3}).$$

The set of real numbers that are both greater than 3 and less than $\tfrac{2}{3}$ is the null set. Hence the desired truth set is the set of all real numbers x such that

$$x < 3 \qquad \text{and} \qquad x > \tfrac{2}{3};$$

that is, such that

$$\tfrac{2}{3} < x < 3.$$

Example 3. Solve

$$\frac{x + 1}{1 - x} < 0, \qquad x \text{ a real number.}$$

By Theorem 3–30 and the corollary to Theorem 3–31,

$$\frac{x + 1}{1 - x} < 0 \Leftrightarrow (x + 1 > 0 \text{ and } 1 - x < 0) \text{ or } (x + 1 < 0 \text{ and } 1 - x > 0)$$
$$\Leftrightarrow (x > -1 \text{ and } x > 1) \text{ or } (x < -1 \text{ and } x < 1)$$
$$\Leftrightarrow (x > 1) \text{ or } (x < -1).$$

Hence, the solution is the set of all real numbers less than -1 or greater than 1.

By Theorem 3–27 we know that $a^2 \geq 0$ for every a in $\mathfrak{F}$. Let us denote the nonnegative element of $\mathfrak{F}$ whose square is a^2, by the numerals

$$\sqrt{a^2} = |a|.$$

The symbol $\sqrt{a^2}$ is read "the principal (nonnegative) square root of a^2" and $|a|$ is read "the absolute value of a." Since $|a| \geq 0$ for every a in $\mathfrak{F}$, we may write

$$a \geq 0 \;\Rightarrow\; |a| = a, \qquad a < 0 \;\Rightarrow\; |a| = -a.$$

REMARK. Two common errors occur frequently on papers of algebra students:

$$(1)\ \sqrt{x^2} = x, \qquad (2)\ \sqrt{4} = \pm 2.$$

The first statement is true only when $x \geq 0$. If $x = -2$, for example, then the statement would read $\sqrt{4} = -2$; but $\sqrt{4}$ is by definition a non-negative number. The student may then argue that $\sqrt{4}$ is either 2 or -2, as in the second statement. The explanation is that every numeral must represent exactly one number, and we define $\sqrt{4}$ to mean 2. Then the student may reply that the square of either 2 or -2 is 4. We agree, and we designate the *nonnegative* square root with the symbol $\sqrt{4}$ and the negative square root by $-\sqrt{4}$.

Example 4. Solve $|x - 2| < 1$, x a real number.

By definition,
$$x - 2 \geq 0 \Rightarrow |x - 2| = x - 2,$$
$$x - 2 < 0 \Rightarrow |x - 2| = -(x - 2).$$

Hence, $|x - 2| < 1$ is equivalent to

$$x - 2 \geq 0 \text{ and } x - 2 < 1 \qquad \text{or} \qquad x - 2 < 0 \text{ and } -(x - 2) < 1,$$

that is, to

$$x < 3 \qquad \text{and} \qquad x > 1, \qquad \text{written } 1 < x < 3.$$

On the number line, $|x - 2|$ represents the distance between the points x and 2. If this distance is to be less than 1, then x must be a point between 1 and 3 (see Fig. 3–1).

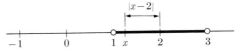

FIGURE 3–1

EXERCISE GROUP 3-3

1. Use O4 and the definition of $>$ to verify the statement:
If $a > b$ and $0 < c$, then $ac > bc$.

2. Prove that if $a \leq b$ and $b \leq a$, then $a = b$.

3. Prove that $a > b$ if and only if there is a positive number c such that $a = b + c$. This property clearly relates $>$ to the operation of addition.

4. Prove that for $a > 0$ and $b > 0$,

$$a^2 > b^2 \qquad \text{if and only if} \qquad a > b.$$

[*Hint:* $a^2 - b^2 = (a - b)(a + b)$.]

5. Prove: If $a < b$, then

$$a < \frac{a + b}{2} < b.$$

6. Prove: If $a \neq 2b$, then

$$\frac{a^2}{4} + b^2 > ab.$$

7. Verify on the number line that

$$|x - a| > b, \ b > 0 \Leftrightarrow x - a > b \text{ or } -(x - a) > b$$
$$\Leftrightarrow x > a + b \text{ or } x < a - b$$

8. Solve the following inequalities (x a real number).

(a) $2x - 4 < 4x - 7$ (b) $5x \geq -3x + 8$

(c) $x(x + 2)(2 - x) > 0$ (d) $(3 - x)(2x - 1) < 0$

(e) $\dfrac{3 + x}{2x + 1} > 0$ (f) $-1 < \dfrac{x - 1}{x + 1} < 3$ (g) $\dfrac{2}{x - 1} > 3$

9. Find the truth sets of the following sentences, where the domain of x is the set of real numbers.

(a) $|x - 2| + 1 = 0$ (b) $x(x - 1) > 0$
(c) $|x - 3| > 2$ (d) $|x + 1| + 2 = 3$
(e) $x^2 - 4x + 3 < 0$ (f) $|x - 2| > 0$
(g) $x^4 - 8x^2 + 15 > 0$ (h) $|x - 1| < 1 \quad \text{and} \quad |x + 1| > 1$
(i) $x^2 + 1 \geq 2x$

10. Find the truth set of each of the following sentences, where x is the first variable, for the indicated domain D of x and y.

(a) $|x| + y = 4,$ $D =$ set of all integers greater than -4
(b) $|x + y| = 4,$ $D =$ set of all integers greater than -4
(c) $|x| + |y| = 4,$ $D =$ set of all integers
(d) $|x| = 3 \quad \text{and} \quad x + y = 1,$ $D = \{1, 2, 3, \ldots\}$
(e) $|x| < 3 \quad \text{and} \quad x + y = 1,$ $D = \{1, 2, 3, \ldots\}$
(f) $(x + y)(y - 2) < 0,$ $D = \{0, 1, 2, 3\}$

11. Draw the graphs of the following sentences for the indicated domain D of each of the variables. (Consider x as the first variable.)

(a) $|x| + y = 4$, D = set of all real numbers
(b) $|x| < 3$ and $|y| \leq 2$, D = set of all integers
(c) $|x| + |y| < 1$, D = set of all real numbers
(d) $xy > 0$, D = set of all integers
(e) $(2x - y)y > 0$, D = set of all real numbers
(f) $|x - y|(x - 1) > 0$, D = set of all real numbers
(g) $(x^2 + y^2 - 4)(x - y) < 0$, D = set of all real numbers

12. Consider the field described in problem 12 of Exercise Group 3–2. If the usual order for positive integers is taken as the order for this field, verify by finding counterexamples that the order axioms are not satisfied.

13. Define an order $\prec$ for $\mathfrak{F}$ by the definition

$$a \prec b \Leftrightarrow |a| < |b|, \qquad a, b \text{ in } \mathfrak{F}.$$

With this definition, do the order axioms hold?

14. Let us take a different set of order axioms:
There exists a subset P of $\mathfrak{F}$ consisting of *positive* numbers such that

(a) for each a in $\mathfrak{F}$ exactly one of the following is true:
a is positive, $a = 0$, $-a$ is positive;
(b) if a, b are positive, so are $a + b$ and ab.

Now define $a > 0$ to mean "a is positive," and $a < b$ to mean "$b - a$ is positive." With these axioms, prove that O1 through O4 follow as theorems.

15. Prove the theorem:
If a, b, c, and d are real numbers such that $b > 0$ and $d > 0$, then

$$\frac{a}{b} < \frac{c}{d} \Leftrightarrow ad < bc.$$

16. Prove $(a, b \text{ in } \mathfrak{F})$:

(a) $|ab| = |a|\,|b|$ (b) $|-a| = |a|$
(c) $-|a| \leq a \leq |a|$
(d) If $b > 0$, then $|a| < b \Leftrightarrow (-b) < a < b$
(e) $|a + b| \leq |a| + |b|$ (f) If $|a| = |b|$, then $a^2 = b^2$

17. Solve (x a real number):

(a) $|x - 2| = |4 - x|$ (b) $|3 - x| = 1$
(c) $|3 - x| < 1$ (d) $|x + 2| = x$
(e) $|x - 2| < 1$ and $|x + 1| < 3$
(f) $|x + 2| < 3$ or $|x - 1| \leq 2$
(g) $|x - 2|^2 + |x - 2| = 2$
(h) $|2x + 1| > 2$ and $|x + 2| < 1$

Chapter 4

Subsystems of the Real Number System

Before completing the list of axioms that describe the abstract system whose model is the set of real numbers (this will be done in Chapter 5), let us show why the list is not already complete. To do this, let us take a different view of the real number model. Instead of looking at real numbers *in toto*, it will be instructive for us to consider certain subsystems of the reals and study the properties of these smaller systems. In the process we shall find one proper subsystem of the reals which itself is an ordered field; thus, the axioms for an ordered field do not completely distinguish the system of real numbers from one of its proper subsystems.

4–1. THE SYSTEM OF NATURAL NUMBERS

If we identify the set $\mathfrak{F}$ with the set R of real numbers, then R contains the element 1, by F5. We also know by Theorem 3–28 that $0 < 1$; that is, 1 is a positive real number. Then $1 + 0 < 1 + 1$, by O3. The real number "$1 + 1$" is called "2." (This is strictly a definition, an arbitrary new symbol naming the same number as the symbol "$1 + 1$.") Thus, 1 < 2, by O2, and $0 < 1 < 2$. In the same way we find that $1 + 1 < 2 + 1$, and, abbreviating "$2 + 1$" to "3" we have $0 < 1 < 2 < 3$. This process is continued by abbreviating "$3 + 1$" to "4," and "$4 + 1$" to "5," etc., where the real number $n + 1$ obtained by adding 1 to the real number n is called the *successor* of n. Thus we construct a set of positive real numbers,
$$N = \{1, 2, 3, 4, \ldots\},$$
called the *natural numbers* with the order $0 < 1 < 2 < 3 < 4 < \cdots$

Intuitively, we can easily visualize the natural numbers, but in order to understand their properties, we need to formulate definitions that do not depend on our intuition.

Definition. The set N of *natural numbers* is the subset of R with the properties:

(a) 1 is in N,

(b) if n is in N, then $n + 1$ is in N, and

(c) if S is any subset of N such that 1 is in S and such that $k + 1$ is in S whenever k is in S, then $S = N$.

At first thought one might argue that (a) and (b) of the definition are enough to characterize the natural numbers. This is not the case. Consider, for example, the set

$$\{\tfrac{1}{2}, 1, \tfrac{3}{2}, 2, \tfrac{5}{2}, 3, \ldots\}.$$

This set satisfies (a) and (b) of the definition but is *not* the set of natural numbers; there is a subset

$$\{1, \tfrac{3}{2}, 2, \tfrac{5}{2}, 3, \ldots\}$$

containing 1 and containing $k + 1$ whenever it contains k, and yet it is not equal to the original set. In effect, N is the *smallest* subset of R with the properties (a) and (b).

Part (c) of the definition describes the conditions under which a set of natural numbers contains *all* the natural numbers. It leads to a powerful property of N that gives us a method for proving other properties of N.

Theorem 4–1 (*Finite induction*). Let $T(n)$ be an open sentence with one variable n in N. If

(a) $T(1)$ is true [1 is in the truth set of $T(n)$] and

(b) $T(k) \Rightarrow T(k + 1)$ [if k is in the truth set of $T(n)$, then $k + 1$ is also in the truth set of $T(n)$], then the truth set of $T(n)$ is the set N.

Proof. Let S be the truth set of $T(n)$ for n in N. Then S is a subset of N. By hypothesis, 1 is in S, and if k is in S, then $k + 1$ is in S. Hence $S = N$, by part (c) of the definition of N.

Theorem 4–2. $1 \leq n$, for every n in N. (This seems like an obvious result, but it must be proved for *every* n in N.)

Proof by finite induction. Let the sentence $T(n)$ be "$1 \leq n$." Then

$$T(1): \ 1 \leq 1; \qquad T(k): \ 1 \leq k; \qquad T(k + 1): \ 1 \leq k + 1.$$

$T(1)$ certainly is true. Hence, 1 is in the truth set of $T(n)$. Next, we prove that $T(k) \Rightarrow T(k + 1)$:

$$1 \leq k, \qquad\qquad\qquad\qquad \text{Hypothesis}$$
$$1 + 1 \leq k + 1, \qquad\qquad\qquad \text{O3}$$
$$1 \leq 1 + 1 \quad \text{and} \quad 1 + 1 \leq k + 1 \Rightarrow 1 \leq k + 1. \qquad \text{O2}$$

We have shown that if k is in the truth set of $T(n)$, then so is $(k + 1)$. Hence the truth set of $T(n)$ contains every natural number, and the theorem is proved.

Theorem 4–3. N is closed under addition.

Proof by finite induction. Let t be any natural number and let $T(n)$ be the sentence, "$t + n$ is a natural number." Then

$$T(1): \quad t + 1 \text{ is in } N; \qquad T(k): \quad t + k \text{ is in } N;$$
$$T(k + 1): \quad t + (k + 1) \text{ is in } N.$$

We know that $T(1)$ is true, by part (b) of the definition of N. Now we prove $T(k) \Rightarrow T(k + 1)$:

$$t + k \text{ is in } N, \qquad\qquad \text{Hypothesis}$$
$$(t + k) + 1 \text{ is in } N, \qquad \text{Part (b) of definition}$$
$$t + (k + 1) \text{ is in } N. \qquad\qquad\qquad \text{F2}$$

Hence $T(n)$ is true for every natural number, and as a result the sum of any two natural numbers is a natural number.

Theorem 4–4. N is closed under multiplication.

Theorem 4–5. Every element of N except 1 is the successor of an element of N.

Proof. Let $T(n)$ be the sentence:

"$n = 1$ or n is the successor of an element of N."

The sentence $T(1)$ is true. (Why?) We must then show that

$$T(k) \Rightarrow T(k + 1).$$

If $k \neq 1$ and k is the successor of an element of N, then there exists an element m in N such that $k = m + 1$. Hence

$$k + 1 = (m + 1) + 1.$$

But if m is in N, then $m + 1$ is in N, and $k + 1$ is also the successor of an element, $m + 1$, in N. Hence, we have shown that $T(1)$ is true and $T(k) \Rightarrow T(k + 1)$. Thus $T(n)$ is true for all n in N.

Theorem 4–6. If n is in N, there is no element of N between $n - 1$ and n.

Theorem 4–7 (*Well ordering*). If n is in N and if S is any subset of N containing a number less than or equal to n, then S contains a least number.

Proof by finite induction. Let $T(n)$ be the sentence, "If $S \subset N$ and S contains a number $t \leq n$, then S contains a least number." The sentence $T(1)$ is true because in this case S contains 1, and 1 is the smallest natural number (Theorem 4–2). Suppose that $T(k)$ is true, and consider $T(k + 1)$. Then if S contains a number t such that $t \leq k + 1$, consider the two possible cases:

(a) $k + 1$ is the smallest element of S, or
(b) there is an element s in S such that $s < k + 1$.

In case (a) S obviously contains a least element. In case (b)

$$s < k + 1 \Rightarrow s \leq k,$$

and since $T(k)$ is true, it follows that S contains a least element. Hence, $T(k + 1)$ is true, and the theorem has been proved.

We define a number p in N to be *prime* if $p > 1$ and if p is not the product of two natural numbers between 1 and p.

Theorem 4–8 (*Unique factorization*). Every natural number greater than 1 is either a prime or the product of primes. The factors of the product are unique.

The proof of this theorem is subtle. (The interested reader should refer to p. 23 of *What is Mathematics?**) Note how the fact that N is a well-ordered set enters into the proof.

Let us summarize what we have learned about the set N (indeed, what intuitive ideas about N we have verified).

(1) Closure. The set N is closed under addition and multiplication. It is not closed under subtraction or division. The reader should verify that $(1 - 2)$ and $\frac{1}{2}$, for example, are not in N.

(2) Finite induction. Let $T(n)$ be an open sentence with one variable n. If $T(1)$ is true, and if $T(k) \Rightarrow T(k + 1)$, then the truth set of $T(n)$ is N.

Example 1. Prove: For any natural number n, $2^n > n$.
Let $T(n)$ be the sentence: $2^n > n$. Then

$$T(1): \quad 2^1 > 1; \qquad T(k): \quad 2^k > k; \qquad T(k + 1): \quad 2^{k+1} > k + 1.$$

$T(1)$ certainly is true. Next, assume $T(k)$ is true and from this deduce that $T(k + 1)$ is true:

$$2^k > k \qquad\qquad \text{Hypothesis}$$
$$2 \cdot 2^k > 2k. \qquad\qquad \text{O4}$$

Now

$$2 \cdot 2^k = 2^{k+1} \quad \text{and} \quad 2k \geq k + 1. \qquad\qquad \text{(Why?)}$$

---

* Richard Courant and Herbert Robbins, Oxford University Press, 1941.

Hence,

$$2^{k+1} > k + 1. \qquad\qquad \text{O2}$$

This completes the proof.

(3) Well-ordering. Every natural number is greater than or equal to 1; that is, 1 is the *least element* of N. An ordered set, each nonempty subset of which has a least element, is called a *well-ordered set*. Hence, the set of natural numbers is well ordered, by Theorem 4–7.

(4) Every natural number greater than 1 can be represented in only one way as the product of primes.

Example 2.

$$108 = 2 \cdot 2 \cdot 3 \cdot 3 \cdot 3 = 2^2 \cdot 3^3 \quad \text{and} \quad 360 = 2 \cdot 2 \cdot 2 \cdot 3 \cdot 3 \cdot 5 = 2^3 \cdot 3^2 \cdot 5.$$

This unique factorization allows us to write the sum

$$\frac{1}{108} + \frac{1}{360} = \frac{1}{2^2 \cdot 3^3} + \frac{1}{2^3 \cdot 3^2 \cdot 5} = \frac{2 \cdot 5}{2^3 \cdot 3^3 \cdot 5} + \frac{3}{2^3 \cdot 3^3 \cdot 5}$$

$$= \frac{13}{2^3 \cdot 3^3 \cdot 5} = \frac{13}{1080}.$$

Note how the "least common denominator" of the fractions is obtained in terms of the prime factorizations of the denominators.

We say that for a and b in N, a is a *factor* of b if there is some natural number c such that $ac = b$. Thus, 3 is a factor of 12 because $3 \cdot 4 = 12$. If a is a factor of b, we say that b is a *multiple* of a. Thus, 12 is a multiple of 3.

If a is a factor of b, we say that a *divides* b (sometimes written $a|b$). It follows that

$$a|b \text{ and } a|c \Rightarrow a|(b + c)$$

and

$$a|b \text{ or } a|c \Rightarrow a|bc.$$

These and other results which the reader can prove are useful in the factorization of polynomials. (See problems 9 through 11.)

Many interesting questions about primes are still unanswered. For example, Euclid showed that the set P of primes is infinite. The proof is easily obtained by contradiction.* But it is still not known whether every even natural number greater than 2 can be written as the sum of two primes; yet no one has exhibited an even number greater than 2 that can-

---

* See G. H. Hardy, *A Mathematician's Apology*, Cambridge University Press, 1940, p. 32.

not be written as such a sum; for example, $42 = 23 + 19$, $68 = 61 + 7$, etc. Also, certain primes occur in pairs as consecutive odd numbers: $3, 5$; $5, 7$; $11, 13$; $17, 19$; $29, 31$; etc. It is not known whether the set of such pairs is infinite.

To make a final comment about N, we note that the set N is infinite, since there is a proper subset of N and a one-to-one correspondence between N and this proper subset. (Describe such a proper subset of N and the correspondence.) We say that a given infinite set is *countable* if it is in one-to-one correspondence with the set N. (This means, of course, that there is a one-to-one mapping of the set onto N.) We shall show in Section 3 that the set of rational numbers is countable.

Even though N is an infinite set, it has limited use in the solutions of equations. Since N lacks closure under subtraction, not even the equation $a + x = b$, where a and b are in N, is guaranteed to have a solution in N. On the other hand, the study of the properties of N has a long and interesting history extending to the present day.

EXERCISE GROUP 4–1

1. Prove in any way you wish that each of the following is true for every natural number n:

(a) $1 + 3 + 5 + 7 + \cdots + (2n - 1) = n^2$

(b) $1^2 + 2^2 + 3^2 + 4^2 + \cdots + n^2 = [n(n + 1)(2n + 1)]/6$

(c) $n^2 + 1 > n$

(d) 2 is a factor of $n^2 + n$

(e) 3 is a factor of $n^3 - n + 3$

(f) 4 is a factor of $7^n - 3^n$. [*Hint:* $7^{k+1} - 3^{k+1} = 7^{k+1} - 3 \cdot 7^k + 3 \cdot 7^k - 3^{k+1}$.]

(g) $1^3 + 2^3 + 3^3 + \cdots + n^3 = (1 + 2 + 3 + \cdots + n)^2$

2. Is the system $(N, +)$ a group? Is $(N, \cdot)$ a group? If not, what is lacking? Which of the axioms F1 through F7, O1 through O4 does the system $(N, +, \cdot)$ satisfy?

3. If 2 is a factor of the natural number n, we say that n is *even*; otherwise, n is *odd*. Prove that for natural numbers a and b:

(a) If a is even and b is odd, then $a + b$ is odd and ab is even.

(b) If a is odd and b is odd, then $a + b$ is even and ab is odd.

(c) If a is even, then a^2 is even.

(d) If a^2 is even, then a is even.

4. Show that if a is in N and if 3 is a factor of a^2, then 3 is a factor of a.

5. Show that if a is in N and b is a positive real number not in N, then $a + b$ is not in N.

6. Prove Theorem 4–4.

7. Prove there is no natural number between 0 and 1. [*Hint:* Use Theorem 4–2.]

8. Prove Theorem 4–6. [*Hint:* Use the result of problem 7 and Theorem 4–5 in a proof by finite induction.]

9. Prove the following for a, b, c in N.

(a) $a|b$ and $a|c \Rightarrow a|(b + c)$
(b) $a|b$ or $a|c \Rightarrow a|bc$
(c) $a|b$ and $a|(b + c) \Rightarrow a|c$
(d) $a|b$ and $a\nmid(b + c) \Rightarrow a\nmid c$ ($a\nmid c$ means that a is not a factor of c).
[*Hint:* Prove by contradiction.]
(e) For p a prime, $p|bc \Rightarrow p|b$ or $p|c$

10. Use the results of problem 9 and unique factorization to find, if possible, two natural numbers b, c whose

(a) product is 24 and sum is 14; [*Hint:* Let $bc = 24$ and $b + c = 14$. Now $24 = 2 \cdot 2 \cdot 2 \cdot 3$. Since $2|24$ and 2 is prime, then $2|b$ or $2|c$. If $2|b$ and $2|(b + c)$, then $2|c$. Hence, $2|b$ and $2|c$. Since $3|24$ and 3 is prime, $3|b$ or $3|c$. But $3\nmid(b + c)$; hence, if $3|b$, then $3\nmid c$, and if $3|c$, then $3\nmid b$. Thus, both b and c contain a factor 2, but only one of b, c contains the factor 3. We conclude that either

$$b = 2 \cdot 3 \quad \text{and} \quad c = 2 \cdot 2$$

or

$$b = 2 \cdot 2 \cdot 3 \quad \text{and} \quad c = 2.$$

The second of these possibilities gives $b + c = 14$.]

(b) product is 72 and sum is 22;
(c) product is 150 and sum is 25;
(d) product is 84 and sum is 24.

11. Use the techniques shown in problem 10 to factor the following polynomials, if possible, into polynomials with coefficients in N:

(a) $x^2 + 8x + 12$ (b) $x^2 + 15x + 56$
(c) $x^2 + 45x + 180$ (d) $x^2 + 32x + 252$

12. We have described the natural numbers as a particular subsystem of the real number system, with its structure obtained from that of the reals. Another approach to the study of the real number system consists of first listing axioms for the system of natural numbers and then extending this system successively to the real number system.

A set of axioms for $(N, +, \cdot)$ must either include or imply F1, F2, F3, F5, finite induction, and the order axioms. The smallest such set of axioms known is the set of *Peano axioms*. For a listing of Peano's axioms for N and the definitions of addition and multiplication of elements of N, read the first chapter of E. Landau's, *Foundations of Analysis.** Explain how, for example, F1 is proved for addition, and how "$<$" is defined and O1 is proved.

---

* Chelsea Publishing Co., 1951, New York.

4-2. THE SYSTEM OF INTEGERS

The set N can be enlarged by attaching to it the real number 0 and the additive inverse of each of the elements of N.

Definition. The subset I of the real numbers consisting of all the natural numbers, 0, and the additive inverses of all the natural numbers, and no others, is called the set of *integers*.

Knowing some properties of N, we may deduce properties of I. First note that the system of integers is ordered by axioms O1 through O4. We know that $2 > 1$ and $-1 < 0$, so that $(-1)(2) < (-1)(1)$ by Theorem 3–26, and hence $-2 < -1 < 0$. In the same way we find that $-3 < -2 < -1 < 0$, and in general

$$\cdots < -4 < -3 < -2 < -1 < 0 < 1 < 2 < 3 < 4 < \cdots$$

But with this order I is *not* well ordered, since there is a nonempty subset of I which has no least element. Such a subset is the set of negative integers. To indicate this we need only show that if n is in this subset, then so is $n - 1$, and $n - 1 < n$. The proof is left as an exercise.

There are real numbers which are not in I, such as $\frac{1}{2}$. This may seem obvious, but it must be proved. The trick is to use properties of an ordered field to show that $\frac{1}{2}$ is a real number that is greater than every negative integer, is not zero, and is less than every positive integer, and hence is not in I. We use Theorem 3–31 to show that

$$2 > 0 \Rightarrow \tfrac{1}{2} > 0;$$
$$1 < 2 \Rightarrow (1)(\tfrac{1}{2}) < (2)(\tfrac{1}{2}) \qquad \text{(Why?)}$$
$$\Rightarrow \tfrac{1}{2} < 1;$$

and

$$\tfrac{1}{2} \neq 0.$$

Hence $\frac{1}{2}$ is not a negative integer, since it is greater than 0; $\frac{1}{2}$ is not zero; and $\frac{1}{2}$ is not a natural number (positive integer) since it is less than 1. Thus, we conclude that $\frac{1}{2}$ is not in I and that I is a *proper* subset of R:

$$N \subset I \subset R, \quad I \neq R, \quad I \neq N.$$

The integers have the following properties:

(1) Closure. The set I is closed under addition, subtraction, and multiplication; it is not closed under division.

Proof. To show that I is closed under addition, we consider various cases. Let a, b be elements of I. Then

$$a \text{ is in } N \qquad \text{or} \qquad a = 0 \qquad \text{or} \qquad -a \text{ is in } N.$$

Case (*a*). If a, b are in N, then $a + b$ is in N, by Theorem 4–3; hence $a + b$ is in I.

Case (*b*). If either a or b is 0, then $a + b$ is in I, by F4.

Case (*c*). If a is in N and $-b$ is in N, then

$$a > -b \quad \text{and} \quad (a + b) + (-b) = a$$
$$\Rightarrow a + b \text{ is in } N \quad \text{(see problem 3, Exercise Group 3–3)}$$
$$\Rightarrow a + b \text{ is in } I;$$

whereas,

$$-b > a \quad \text{and} \quad a + [-(a + b)] = (-b)$$
$$\Rightarrow -(a + b) \text{ is in } N \quad \text{(see problem 3,}$$
$$\text{Exercise Group 3–3)}$$
$$\Rightarrow a + b \text{ is in } I;$$

and finally,

$$a = -b \Rightarrow a + b = 0$$
$$\Rightarrow a + b \text{ is in } I.$$

Case (*d*). If $-a$ and $-b$ are in N, then $a + b = -[(-a) + (-b)]$. But $(-a) + (-b)$ is in N, by Theorem 4–3. Hence, $a + b$ is in I.

The reader is invited to use a similar procedure to show that I is closed under multiplication.

By definition, subtraction is described by

$$a - b = a + (-b).$$

If a and b are in I, then a and $-b$ are in I; hence $a - b$ is in I, by the closure of I under addition. Thus, I is closed under subtraction.

Finally, I is not closed under division. Here is a counterexample: "$1 \div 2$" is defined to be "$1 \cdot (\frac{1}{2})$"; but $\frac{1}{2}$ is not in I.

In the transition from N to I, we gained the property of closure under subtraction. Now for any a and b in I there is a unique solution of $a + x = b$ in I, namely $b - a$; but there is no solution in I guaranteed for $ax = b$.

The system $(I, +)$ is a commutative group. The reader should verify this fact. Moreover, the system $(I, +, \cdot)$ is a commutative ring.

(2) Unique factorization. Each integer other than -1, 0, 1 can be written as the product of primes and 1 or -1 in only one way; that is, integers have the property of *unique factorization*.

(3) Countability. The set of integers is *countable*.

Proof. We may obtain a one-to-one mapping of I onto N in the following manner:

$$\frac{I \quad\quad N}{}$$

$$0 \leftrightarrow 1$$
$$1 \leftrightarrow 2$$
$$-1 \leftrightarrow 3$$
$$2 \leftrightarrow 4$$
$$-2 \leftrightarrow 5,$$
$$\text{etc.}$$

(Under this mapping which integer corresponds to the natural number 75?). There are many other possible one-to-one mappings of I onto N. Describe one of them.

(4) Division algorithm. Given any two integers a and b, $b \neq 0$, there can be found an integer c and a natural number r such that

$$a = bc + r, \quad \text{where} \quad 0 \leq r < |b|.$$

Proof. If b is any nonzero integer, the integers

$$\ldots, \; -2b, \; -b, \; 0, \; b, \; 2b, \; \ldots$$

are *multiples* of b. Given any integer a, we know that it is either equal to one of the multiples of b or it lies between two successive multiples of b. In the latter case, we mean that there is an integer c such that (for b positive)

$$bc < a < b(c + 1);$$

that is,

$$a - bc > 0 \quad \text{and} \quad a - bc < b.$$

Thus, we may set $a - bc = r$, that is, $a = bc + r$, where r is an integer such that $0 < r < b$. If a is a multiple of b, then $a = bc + r$, with $r = 0$. If b is any nonzero integer, we see that there is an integer c such that

$$a = bc + r, \quad \text{where} \quad 0 \leq r < |b|.$$

Here we have the important *division algorithm* which guarantees that for any two integers a and b, $b \neq 0$, there is an integer c, called the *quotient*, and a nonnegative integer r, called the *remainder*, such that

$$a = bc + r \quad \text{and} \quad 0 \leq r < |b|.$$

For example, if $a = 21$ and $b = -5$, we may write $21 = (-5)(-4) + 1$. If $a = -2$ and $b = 5$, then $-2 = (5)(-1) + 3$. If $a = -21$ and $b = 7$, then $-21 = (7)(-3) + 0$.

(5) Decimal representation. The division algorithm for integers allows us to write any integer in a *decimal representation:** Given a positive integer d, there are integers c_0, c_1, c_2, . . . , c_n from the set $\{0, 1, 2, 3, \ldots, 9\}$ such that

$$d = c_0 + c_1 10 + c_2 10^2 + \cdots + c_n 10^n.$$

The c's are called *digits*, and n is some natural number or 0.

Proof. To show that such a representation is always possible, apply the division algorithm to d and 10, obtaining

$$d = d_1 10 + c_0, \qquad 0 \le c_0 < 10.$$

If $d_1 > 9$, then apply the algorithm again to d_1 and 10, getting

$$d_1 = d_2 10 + c_1, \qquad 0 \le c_1 < 10.$$

Continue this process until a quotient d_n less than 10 is obtained (why will this happen in a finite number of steps?):

$$d_{n-1} = d_n 10 + c_{n-1}, \qquad 0 \le c_{n-1} < 10,$$
$$d_n = c_n, \qquad 0 \le c_n < 10.$$

Then, upon eliminating $d_1, d_2, \ldots, d_n$ from these equations, we have

$$d = c_0 + c_1 10 + c_2 10^2 + \cdots + c_n 10^n.$$

If d is a negative integer, multiply the decimal representation of $|d|$ by -1.

Although it is customary to restrict the digits to integers from the set $\{0, 1, 2, \ldots, 9\}$, we may let the digits be taken from any set of the form $\{0, 1, 2, 3, \ldots, (p - 1)\}$, with $p > 1$, and represent d as

$$d = c_0 + c_1 p + c_2 p^2 + \cdots + c_n p^n.$$

For example, in the *ternary* representation of d, we select the digits from $\{0, 1, 2\}$. Then $11 = 3 \cdot 3 + 2$ and $3 = 3 \cdot 1 + 0$; hence,

$$11 = 2 + 0 \cdot 3 + 1 \cdot 3^2,$$

which we abbreviate to $(102)_{\text{three}}$, read "one-oh-two, base three."

In summary, when we extend the set N to the set I, we lose certain properties and gain others. The properties of finite induction and well ordering are lost. On the other hand, we gain the important property of closure under subtraction. It should be noted in passing that computa-

---

* A *representation* of a number is a manner of naming the number.

tions with, and representations of, natural numbers are extremely cumbersome without the services of the integer zero. Without a device for representing zero, any form of representation of integers must be accumulative, as the Roman numerals are. Only with the introduction of zero can representation be positional, that is, in terms of coefficients of powers of some integer. The fact that every integer can be written as a *terminating* decimal is of great importance in calculations. ("Terminating" means that only a finite number of coefficient digits is required in the representation.)

EXERCISE GROUP 4–2

1. If for integers we take definitions of *factor* and *multiple* similar to those for natural numbers, then the integer a is even if there is an integer c such that $a = 2c$.

   (a) Is 0 an even integer?
   (b) If a is an odd integer and b is an odd integer, is ab an odd integer?
   (c) If a is an integer and a^2 is even, prove that a is even.

2. For integers a and b, recall that $a|b$ means "a is a factor of b." Define the *greatest common divisor* of a and b, written (a, b), as the greatest positive integer d such that $d|a$ and $d|b$. [Note that for any e such that $e|a$ and $e|b$, we have $e|(a, b)$.]

   (a) Compute $(-360, 90)$; $(30, 54)$; $(73, -162)$.
   (b) If $a > 0$, prove that $(ab, ac) = a \cdot (b, c)$.

3. Is the set of negative integers closed under addition? subtraction? multiplication?

4. By $(326)_{ten}$ we mean $6 + 2 \cdot 10 + 3 \cdot 10^2$.

   (a) Convert $(4152)_{six}$ to the "ten" scale, that is, to decimal representation.
   (b) Convert $(101100)_{two}$ to decimal representation.
   (c) Convert $(326)_{ten}$ to a representation in the "three" scale.
   (d) Convert $(326)_{ten}$ to the "nine" scale.

5. Is the system $(I, +)$ a group? Is $(I, \cdot)$ a group? If not, explain what is lacking.

6. Is the system $(I, +, \cdot)$ a field? If not, what is lacking?

7. Explain the usual algorithms for adding, multiplying, "carrying," and subtracting integers in terms of decimal representation.

8. (a) Prove that with the ordering given by axioms O1 through O4, the set of integers is not well ordered. [*Hint:* Show that if n is a negative integer, so is $n - 1$.]
   (b) Define a different ordering of I for which I *is* well ordered.

9. Consider the set of integers

$$T = \{4, 7, 10, 13, 16, \ldots, 3k + 1, \ldots\}.$$

Let us define a prime in this set to be an element that cannot be obtained as the product of two elements in T. Thus, 4, 7, 10, 13, 19, 22, 25, 31, etc., are primes in T, whereas 16, 28, 40, etc., are composites in T. Can every composite in T be factored *uniquely* into products of primes in T?

10. Consider the ring $(S, \oplus, \odot)$, where $S = \{0, 1, 2, 3, 4, 5\}$, $a \oplus b$ is the remainder when $a + b$ is divided by 6, and $a \odot b$ is the remainder when ab is divided by 6.

(a) Determine which elements of S (other than 0, 1) are primes.
(b) Does this system have the property of unique factorization?

11. Prove that I is closed under multiplication.

12. (Continuation of problem 12 of Exercise Group 4–1.) We may view the integers as an extension of the natural numbers in the following way. Consider the set Z of all ordered pairs of natural numbers:

$$(a, b) \text{ is an element of } Z \Leftrightarrow a, b \text{ are in } N.$$

Define equivalence $=$, addition $\oplus$, and multiplication $\odot$ of elements in Z as follows.

If (a, b) and (c, d) are in Z, then

$$(a, b) = (c, d) \Leftrightarrow a + d = b + c,$$
$$(a, b) \oplus (c, d) = (a + c, b + d),$$
$$(a, b) \odot (c, d) = (ac + bd, ad + bc).$$

(a) Show that $=$ is an equivalence and that the operations are well defined.
(b) Show that $\oplus$ and $\odot$ are commutative and associative.
(c) Show that $\odot$ is distributive through $\oplus$.
(d) Show that (a, a) is an identity for $\oplus$; $(a + 1, a)$ is an identity for $\odot$, where a is any natural number.
(e) Show that (b, a) is an additive inverse of (a, b).
(f) Show that $(a + b, a) = (c + b, c)$, $(a, a) = (c, c)$, $(a, a + b) = (c, c + b)$ for any a, c in N. (We denote a class of equal pairs in Z by any of the equal pairs.)
(g) Let Z_0 be the set of all equivalence classes in Z. Then there is a mapping f of Z_0 onto I such that:
the class $(a + b, a)$ for any a corresponds to the positive integer b,
the class (a, a) for any a corresponds to the integer 0, and
the class $(a, a + b)$ for any a corresponds to the negative integer $-b$.
This mapping is one-to-one, as well as onto, and f pairs sums and products in Z_0 with sums and products of corresponding elements in I. Then $(Z_0, \oplus, \odot)$ is isomorphic to $(I, +, \cdot)$, and the two systems are considered to be the same system. We write b in place of the class $(a + b, a)$, 0 in place of the class (a, a), and $-b$ in place of the class $(a, a + b)$.

Consider the subset of Z_0 consisting of all classes of elements of the form $(a + b, a)$ for any a, b in N. Call this subset P. Show that the above mapping f, considered as a mapping of P into N, is one-to-one and onto, and that f pairs sums and products of elements of P with sums and products of corresponding elements of N; that is, show that the set P of positive integers is isomorphic to the set N of natural numbers.

(h) Use the definitions of addition and multiplication above to compute: $5 + (-2)$, $(-6) + (-3)$, $5 + (-7)$, $(6)(-4)$, $(-2)(-5)$.

For example,

$$5 + (-2) \leftrightarrow (a + 5, a) \oplus (a, a + 2)$$
$$= (2a + 5, 2a + 2)$$
$$= (2a + 2 + 3, 2a + 2) \leftrightarrow 3.$$

Hence, $5 + (-2) = 3$.

13. The system $(I, +, \cdot)$ is a commutative ring with an identity and no proper divisors of zero. Such a ring is called an *integral domain*. We sometimes call a ring with no proper (nonzero) divisors of zero a *regular* ring:

A ring S is regular if for any elements a, b in S,

$$ab = 0 \Leftrightarrow a = 0 \text{ or } b = 0.$$

(a) Prove that if a, b, c are elements of a regular ring, then $c \neq 0$, $ac = bc \Rightarrow a = b$ (right cancellation).

(b) Prove that if p, q, r are elements of a ring S with the right cancellation property, then S is regular. (Note that not every ring is regular but that all integral domains are regular rings. Remember also that regularity and cancellation are equivalent properties in a ring.)

14. Using results suggested by problems 9 through 12 and problem 18 in Exercise Group 1–2, find an example of a ring that:

(a) is commutative and regular, but has no multiplicative identity,
(b) is commutative and has a multiplicative identity, but is not regular,
(c) has a multiplicative identity, but is neither commutative nor regular,
(d) is not commutative, not regular, and has no multiplicative identity.

4–3. THE SYSTEM OF RATIONAL NUMBERS

The system of integers can be extended to an even larger system as follows. Consider any integer q in I such that $q \neq 0$. Then by F7 there is a number $1/q$ in R. If p is an integer, the product

$$p\left(\frac{1}{q}\right) = \frac{p}{q}$$

is a real number, since the set R is closed under multiplication.

The subset of R consisting of all real numbers, and only those, that can be represented in the form p/q, where p and q are *integers*, $q \neq 0$, is called the set F of *rational numbers*.

The adjective "rational" here implies "ratio," and not the usual dictionary meaning "reasonable" or "sensible."

At this point we should comment on the uses of the words "fraction" and "rational number." It must be remembered that a fraction is not a number; it is a symbol that represents a number. By definition, a fraction has the form

$$\frac{x}{y}, \quad y \neq 0,$$

for any x and y; that is, it indicates a division process. In particular, if x and y represent *integers*, then the resulting fraction represents a *rational number*. For example, the fraction "$\frac{2}{3}$" represents a rational number, whereas "$\sqrt{2}/3$" represents a number which, as we shall show, is not rational. Note that since the fraction "$\sqrt{3}/\sqrt{12}$" represents the same number as the fraction "$\frac{1}{2}$," it represents a rational number. Thus we see that certain fractions name rational numbers and others do not, but every rational number can be represented as a fraction whose numerator and denominator both name integers.

The representation of a rational number is by no means unique. Theorem 3–17, which states that $ab/cb = a/c$, shows that each rational number has infinitely many fractional names. For example,

$$\frac{3}{2} = \frac{6}{4} = \frac{9}{6} = \frac{12}{8} = \cdots = \frac{-3}{-2} = \frac{-6}{-4} = \frac{-9}{-6} = \cdots,$$

and each of these is a numeral for the number $\frac{3}{2}$.

A student who is mystified by "computation with fractions" usually fails to understand that

(1) for any real number a, $a \cdot 1 = 1 \cdot a = a$;

(2) each of the following is a numeral for 1:

$$1, \frac{1}{1}, \frac{2}{2}, \frac{3}{3}, \cdots, \frac{-1}{-1}, \frac{-2}{-2}, \cdots, \frac{b}{b}, \quad b \neq 0.$$

(Why is it true that $1 = \frac{1}{1}$? *Hint:* Apply problem 2, of Exercise Group 3–2, for certain values of a and b.)

It should be clear that every integer n is a rational number (but not conversely):

$$n = n \cdot 1 \text{ and } n \cdot 1 = n \cdot \frac{1}{1} \text{ and } n \cdot \frac{1}{1} = \frac{n}{1} \Rightarrow n = \frac{n}{1},$$

and, hence, n may be represented in the form a/b, where a and b are integers, $b \neq 0$. From this we conclude that $I \subset F$. Since $\frac{1}{2}$ is in F but not in I, we have $I \neq F$. Thus, the integers are a proper subset of the rational numbers.

Some of the properties of the system $(F, +, \cdot)$ are:

(1) Closure. The set F is closed under addition, subtraction, and multiplication. The quotient of a rational number by a nonzero rational number is a rational number. Thus, with division by zero excluded, F is also closed under division.

Proof. Theorem 3–18 with a, b, c, d integers, $b \neq 0$, $d \neq 0$, implies that the sum of the rational numbers a/b and c/d is the number

$$\frac{ad + bc}{bd}.$$

But the set of integers is closed under addition and multiplication, so that $ad + bc$ and bd are integers, with $bd \neq 0$. (Why?) We conclude that

$$\frac{ad + bc}{bd}$$

is in F, and F is closed under addition. Similarly, Theorem 3–16′ shows that F is closed under multiplication. With $r - s$ defined as $r + (-s)$, the reader can easily show that F is closed under subtraction. Finally, Theorem 3–19, with a, b, c, d integers and $b \neq 0$, $c \neq 0$, and $d \neq 0$, implies that F is closed under division, where the restriction $c \neq 0$ excludes division by zero.

We know that every rational number is a real number. Hence, $F \subset R$. Moreover, if r and s are in F, so are $r + s$, $r - s$, rs, and r/s (if $s \neq 0$). The elements of F satisfy axioms F1 through F7 and O1 through O4, so that the system $(F, +, \cdot)$ is an ordered field. Later we shall show that $F \neq R$; that is, there are real numbers that are not rational. As a result, it will be demonstrated that F is a *proper* subfield of R.

(2) Countability. The set F is *countable*.

Proof. Remembering that any rational number may be written with a positive denominator, write the rational numbers in the array form shown in Table 4–1.

Starting with $0/1$ and proceeding through the array as indicated by the arrows, we eventually encounter any given rational number whose numerator is an integer (in some column) and whose denominator is a positive integer (in some row). Thus we define a one-to-one mapping of F onto N by associating each rational number along the indicated path with a natural number, skipping a numeral if the number it represents has been encountered previously (circled), as follows:

$$
\begin{array}{c|ccccccccc}
F & \dfrac{0}{1} & \dfrac{1}{1} & \dfrac{1}{2} & \dfrac{-1}{2} & \dfrac{-1}{1} & \dfrac{-2}{1} & \dfrac{-2}{3} & \dfrac{-1}{3} & \dfrac{1}{3} & \cdots \\
 & \updownarrow & \updownarrow & \updownarrow & \updownarrow & \updownarrow & \updownarrow & \updownarrow & \updownarrow & \updownarrow \\
N & 1 & 2 & 3 & 4 & 5 & 6 & 7 & 8 & 9 & \cdots
\end{array}
$$

TABLE 4-1

$$\cdots \frac{-p}{1} \cdots \frac{-4}{1} \leftarrow \frac{-3}{1} \quad \frac{-2}{1} \leftarrow \frac{-1}{1} \quad \frac{0}{1} \rightarrow \frac{1}{1} \quad \frac{2}{1} \rightarrow \frac{3}{1} \quad \frac{4}{1} \rightarrow \cdots \frac{p}{1} \cdots$$

$$\cdots \frac{-p}{2} \cdots \left(\frac{-4}{2}\right) \quad \frac{-3}{2} \quad \left(\frac{-2}{2}\right) \quad \frac{-1}{2} \leftarrow \left(\frac{0}{2}\right) \leftarrow \frac{1}{2} \quad \left(\frac{2}{2}\right) \quad \frac{3}{2} \quad \left(\frac{4}{2}\right) \cdots \frac{p}{2} \cdots$$

$$\cdots \frac{-p}{3} \cdots \frac{-4}{3} \quad \left(\frac{-3}{3}\right) \quad \frac{-2}{3} \rightarrow \frac{-1}{3} \rightarrow \left(\frac{0}{3}\right) \rightarrow \frac{1}{3} \rightarrow \frac{2}{3} \quad \left(\frac{3}{3}\right) \quad \frac{4}{3} \cdots \frac{p}{3} \cdots$$

$$\cdots \frac{-p}{4} \cdots \left(\frac{-4}{4}\right) \quad \frac{-3}{4} \leftarrow \left(\frac{-2}{4}\right) \leftarrow \frac{-1}{4} \leftarrow \left(\frac{0}{4}\right) \leftarrow \frac{1}{4} \leftarrow \left(\frac{2}{4}\right) \leftarrow \frac{3}{4} \quad \left(\frac{4}{4}\right) \cdots \frac{p}{4} \cdots$$

$$\cdots \frac{-p}{5} \cdots \frac{-4}{5} \rightarrow \frac{-3}{5} \rightarrow \frac{-2}{5} \rightarrow \frac{-1}{5} \rightarrow \left(\frac{0}{5}\right) \rightarrow \frac{1}{5} \rightarrow \frac{2}{5} \rightarrow \frac{3}{5} \rightarrow \frac{4}{5} \rightarrow \cdots \frac{p}{5} \cdots$$

$$\cdots \frac{-p}{q} \quad \frac{-4}{q} \quad \frac{-3}{q} \quad \frac{-2}{q} \quad \frac{-1}{q} \quad \frac{0}{q} \quad \frac{1}{q} \quad \frac{2}{q} \quad \frac{3}{q} \quad \frac{4}{q} \quad \cdots \frac{p}{q} \cdots$$

Under this mapping each rational number corresponds to one natural number, and each natural number corresponds to one rational number.

(3) Decimal representation. Every rational number r can be *represented as a decimal.*

To illustrate the meaning of this statement, let us obtain such a representation of the rational number $\frac{13}{8}$. By the division algorithm,

$$13 = 8 \cdot 1 + 5, \qquad 5 < 8,$$
$$5 \cdot 10 = 8 \cdot 6 + 2, \qquad 2 < 8,$$
$$2 \cdot 10 = 8 \cdot 2 + 4, \qquad 4 < 8,$$
$$4 \cdot 10 = 8 \cdot 5 + 0.$$

Upon dividing by 8 and successive powers of 10, we obtain

$$\frac{13}{8} = 1 + \frac{5}{8};$$

$$\frac{5}{8} = \frac{6}{10} + \frac{2}{8}\left(\frac{1}{10}\right); \qquad \frac{13}{8} = 1 + \frac{6}{10} + \frac{2}{8}\left(\frac{1}{10}\right),$$

$$\frac{2}{80} = \frac{2}{10^2} + \frac{4}{8}\left(\frac{1}{10^2}\right); \qquad \frac{13}{8} = 1 + \frac{6}{10} + \frac{2}{10^2} + \frac{4}{8}\left(\frac{1}{10^2}\right),$$

$$\frac{4}{800} = \frac{5}{10^3} + 0; \qquad \frac{13}{8} = 1 + \frac{6}{10} + \frac{2}{10^2} + \frac{5}{10^3},$$

and from these equalities we obtain the set of inequalities:

$$1 + \frac{6}{10} \leq \frac{13}{8} = 1 + \frac{6}{10} + \frac{2}{8}\left(\frac{1}{10}\right) < 1 + \frac{7}{10},$$

$$1 + \frac{6}{10} + \frac{2}{10^2} \leq \frac{13}{8} = 1 + \frac{6}{10} + \frac{2}{10^2} + \frac{4}{8}\left(\frac{1}{10^2}\right) < 1 + \frac{6}{10} + \frac{3}{10^2}$$

$$1 + \frac{6}{10} + \frac{2}{10^2} + \frac{5}{10^3} = \frac{13}{8}.$$

We abbreviate this to

$$\tfrac{13}{8} = 1.625.$$

Note that for this rational number, one of the remainders in the division algorithm is zero and that the decimal representation therefore *terminates*; that is, the set of inequalities terminates in an equality. Of course, the whole process is abbreviated in arithmetic to the familiar scheme shown on the right. Note how the division algorithm justifies this scheme.

```
        1.625
  8)13.000
     8
     ─
     50
     48
     ──
      20
      16
      ──
       40
       40
       ──
```

The reader may wonder why we bothered to write the set of inequalities, especially since the decimal representation terminated. The example below will show the need for inequalities. Let us attempt to represent the rational number $\frac{4}{11}$ as a decimal; again, we will use the division algorithm,

$$4 \cdot 10 = 11 \cdot 3 + 7, \qquad 7 < 11,$$
$$7 \cdot 10 = 11 \cdot 6 + 4, \qquad 4 < 11,$$
$$4 \cdot 10 = 11 \cdot 3 + 7, \qquad 7 < 11,$$
$$7 \cdot 10 = 11 \cdot 6 + 4, \qquad 4 < 11,$$
$$\vdots \qquad \qquad \vdots$$

Dividing by 11 and successive powers of 10, we get

$$\frac{4}{11} = \frac{3}{10} + \frac{7}{11}\left(\frac{1}{10}\right);$$

$$\frac{7}{110} = \frac{6}{10^2} + \frac{4}{11}\left(\frac{1}{10^2}\right); \qquad \frac{4}{11} = \frac{3}{10} + \frac{6}{10^2} + \frac{4}{11}\left(\frac{1}{10^2}\right),$$

$$\frac{4}{1100} = \frac{3}{10^3} + \frac{7}{11}\left(\frac{1}{10^3}\right); \qquad \frac{4}{11} = \frac{3}{10} + \frac{6}{10^2} + \frac{3}{10^3} + \frac{7}{11}\left(\frac{1}{10^3}\right),$$

$$\frac{7}{11000} = \frac{6}{10^4} + \frac{4}{11}\left(\frac{1}{10^4}\right); \qquad \frac{4}{11} = \frac{3}{10} + \frac{6}{10^2} + \frac{3}{10^3} + \frac{6}{10^4} + \frac{4}{11}\left(\frac{1}{10^4}\right),$$

etc.

Note that the remainders repeat in the pattern 7, 4, 7, 4, . . . , and no remainder can be zero. The resulting *infinite* set of equalities gives rise to the corresponding *infinite* set of inequalities:

$$\frac{3}{10} \le \frac{4}{11} < \frac{4}{10},$$

$$\frac{3}{10} + \frac{6}{10^2} \le \frac{4}{11} < \frac{3}{10} + \frac{7}{10^2},$$

$$\frac{3}{10} + \frac{6}{10^2} + \frac{3}{10^3} \le \frac{4}{11} < \frac{3}{10} + \frac{6}{10^2} + \frac{4}{10^3},$$

$$\frac{3}{10} + \frac{6}{10^2} + \frac{3}{10^3} + \frac{6}{10^4} \le \frac{4}{11} < \frac{3}{10} + \frac{6}{10^2} + \frac{3}{10^3} + \frac{7}{10^4},$$

etc.

When we say that $\frac{4}{11}$ *is represented by the infinite decimal* .3636..., we mean that $\frac{4}{11}$ satisfies *every* inequality in the above infinite set of inequalities.

The fact that the remainders in the above division algorithm repeat with a fixed pattern leads us to call the resulting decimal representation *periodic*, and we indicate the set of repeating digits by superscript dots; for example,

$$\tfrac{4}{11} = .3636\ldots = .\dot{3}\dot{6}.$$

As we have seen, some rational numbers have infinite decimal representations and some terminate. We shall now show that every rational number has a decimal representation, either terminating or infinite, and if the decimal representation of a rational number is infinite, it is also periodic. Consider the positive rational number p/q, where p and q are positive integers without common factors. The division algorithm guarantees the existence of integers c and r_0 such that

$$p = qc + r_0, \qquad 0 \le r_0 < q.$$

Dividing by q, we have

$$\frac{p}{q} = c + \frac{r_0}{q}, \qquad 0 < \frac{r_0}{q} < 1.$$

If $r_0 = 0$, the decimal terminates. If $r_0 \ne 0$, apply the algorithm to the positive integers $10r_0$ and q:

$$10r_0 = qd_1 + r_1, \qquad 0 \le r_1 < q,$$

for some integer d_1. Since $r_0 < q$,

$$10r_0 = qd_1 + r_1 < 10q$$

implies that $d_1 < 10$. Again, dividing by $10q$, we have

$$\frac{r_0}{q} = \frac{d_1}{10} + \frac{r_1}{10q}; \qquad \frac{p}{q} = c + \frac{d_1}{10} + \frac{r_1}{10q}.$$

Now if $r_1 = 0$, the decimal representation of p/q exists and terminates. If $r_1 \neq 0$, then $r_1/q < 1$ and

$$c + \frac{d_1}{10} \leq \frac{p}{q} = c + \frac{d_1}{10} + \frac{r_1}{10q} < c + \frac{d_1 + 1}{10}.$$

Now apply the algorithm to $10r_1$ and q:

$$10r_1 = qd_2 + r_2, \qquad 0 \leq r_2 < q,$$

for some integer d_2. Again we can show that $d_2 < 10$ and that

$$\frac{r_1}{10q} = \frac{d_2}{10^2} + \frac{r_2}{10^2 q}; \qquad \frac{p}{q} = c + \frac{d_1}{10} + \frac{d_2}{10^2} + \frac{r_2}{10^2 q}.$$

Now $r_2/q < 1$ and

$$c + \frac{d_1}{10} + \frac{d_2}{10^2} \leq \frac{p}{q} = c + \frac{d_1}{10} + \frac{d_2}{10^2} + \frac{r_2}{10^2 q} < c + \frac{d_1}{10} + \frac{d_2 + 1}{10^2}.$$

If $r_2 \neq 0$ we continue the process until some remainder r_i is zero, in which case the decimal exists and terminates, or until some remainder r_k is equal to a previous remainder r_j, $j < k$. The latter must occur if no r_i is zero because there are no more than $q - 1$ possible nonzero remainders upon division by q. In this case there is a decimal representation of p/q which never terminates, and the set of digits $d_j d_{j+1} \ldots d_{k-1}$ will repeat without end.

Thus, if a rational number r has an infinite decimal representation, it is periodic. By a *decimal representation* of r we mean that for *every* natural number k, r satisfies the inequality

$$c + \frac{d_1}{10} + \cdots + \frac{d_k}{10^k} \leq r < c + \frac{d_1}{10} + \cdots + \frac{d_k + 1}{10^k},$$

where each d_i is some integer in the set

$$\{0, 1, 2, \ldots, 9\}.$$

Again, we should point out that the digits of the representation of r may be restricted to any set of the form

$$\{0, 1, \ldots, (b - 1)\}, \qquad b > 1.$$

The development of the representation given above for $b = 10$ is quite general and does not depend in any way on the scale or base b of representation. For example, the rational number $\frac{4}{3}$ may be represented in the "five" scale as follows:

$$4 = 3 \cdot 1 + 1 \Rightarrow \frac{4}{3} = 1 + \frac{1}{3} \Rightarrow 1 \leq \frac{4}{3} < 2,$$

$$5 \cdot 1 = 3 \cdot 1 + 2 \Rightarrow \frac{1}{3} = \frac{1}{5} + \frac{2}{5 \cdot 3} \Rightarrow 1 + \frac{1}{5} \leq \frac{4}{3} < 1 + \frac{2}{5},$$

$$5 \cdot 2 = 3 \cdot 3 + 1 \Rightarrow \frac{2}{3} = \frac{3}{5} + \frac{1}{5 \cdot 3} \Rightarrow 1 + \frac{1}{5} + \frac{3}{5^2} \leq \frac{4}{3} < 1 + \frac{1}{5} + \frac{4}{5^2},$$

etc.

Hence

$$\frac{4}{3} = 1.1313\ldots_{\text{five}} = 1.1\dot{3}_{\text{five}}.$$

It can also be shown (see Chapter 6) that every periodic decimal represents a rational number and only one rational number.

(4) Density. The set of rational numbers is *dense*; that is, for any two rational numbers u and v, there is a rational number w between u and v.

Viewed on the number line, this property asserts that any two points with rational number coordinates, no matter how close together, have a point between them with a rational coordinate. However, there is no end to this argument; this implies that between any two rational numbers there are *infinitely many* rational numbers. The proof of this property follows immediately from problem 5 in Exercise Group 3–3. If a and b are rational numbers such that $a < b$, then

$$a < \frac{a + b}{2} < b.$$

Since $\dfrac{a + b}{2}$ is also rational if a and b are rational, the density property is established. For the same reason the set of real numbers is also dense.

At this point in the development, we have not found any difference between the rational and real number systems. Each is an ordered field and each is a dense set. At first thought one might suspect that there is no difference; it would appear that F, being dense, corresponds to the set of all points on the number line. There would seem to be no "room" between the rationals for other numbers. This is not the case. When we introduce a final axiom in Chapter 5 for the real number system, it will be possible to prove, for example, that there is a positive *real* number x such that $x^2 = 2$, that is, $x = \sqrt{2}$. We shall now prove that there is *no rational* number x such that $x^2 = 2$.

Theorem 4–9. There is no rational number x such that $x^2 = 2$; that is, there do not exist two integers a and b without common factors such that

$$x^2 = \left(\frac{a}{b}\right)^2 = 2.$$

Proof. We shall develop a proof by contradiction. Assume as part of the hypothesis that there are two integers a and b, *without common factors*, such that $(a/b)^2 = 2$. We underline the restriction "without common factors" because by Theorem 3–17 it is always possible to reduce a rational number a/b to such a form. Then

$$\left(\frac{a}{b}\right)^2 = 2 \Rightarrow a^2 = 2b^2.$$

Since b is an integer, so is b^2. Thus a^2 is an even integer. By the result of problem 1(c) in Exercise Group 4–2, a is also an *even* integer; thus, we may write

$$a = 2c, \quad \text{for some integer } c.$$

Then

$$a = 2c \Rightarrow a^2 = 4c^2.$$

We now have $a^2 = 4c^2$ and $a^2 = 2b^2$, so that $2b^2 = 4c^2$; that is, $b^2 = 2c^2$. But c^2 is an integer, so that b^2 is an even integer. This means that b is also an *even* integer. We have arrived at a contradiction, for if a and b are both even integers, they must have the common factor 2, contrary to our original requirement. Thus, there is no rational number x such that $x^2 = 2$.

Real numbers that are not rational are called *irrational* numbers. Thus, $\sqrt{2}$ is an irrational number.

Let us summarize what we have found. In the transition from the integers to the rational numbers, we lost some properties; that is, some of the properties of the integers are not shared by the rationals. For one, we do not have unique factorization of rational numbers: if r and s are *any* nonzero rational numbers, then r is a factor of s and s is a factor of r; that is, there exist rational numbers u and v such that $s = ru$ and $r = sv$. Another property that we lost is the one of terminating decimal representation. However, we gained the important properties of closure under division (zero excluded) and density.

This concludes the discussion of three proper subsystems of the reals:

$$N \subset I \subset F \subset R.$$

Which properties of F are shared by R? Certainly R has the same closure properties as F. It will be shown (in Chapter 6) that R is *not* countable; R is also dense, and its elements can be represented in decimal form, although these decimals will be shown to be *nonperiodic* in general. What new properties does R have? It will be shown that the set of *positive* real numbers is closed under the extraction of a root. This means, for example, that for a in R the equation $x^2 = a$ has a solution in R if $a > 0$. The most important new property, from the standpoint of analysis and geometry, is the fact that R is *complete*. This will be the theme of the next chapter.

EXERCISE GROUP 4–3

1. Since $(F, +, \cdot)$ is an ordered field, it must be possible to decide which of two given rational numbers is greater. Use the result of problem 15 in Exercise Group 3–3, with a, b, c, d integers, to rank the numbers

$$\frac{-37}{61}, \quad \frac{4}{5}, \quad \frac{12}{-20}, \quad \frac{47}{59}$$

from greatest to least. (Note that if q is a negative integer,

$$\frac{p}{q} = \left(\frac{-1}{-1}\right)\left(\frac{p}{q}\right) = \frac{-p}{-q},$$

where $-q$ is a positive integer.)

2. The rational number $(\frac{3}{16})_{\text{ten}}$ can be represented as the decimal

$$\frac{1}{10} + \frac{8}{10^2} + \frac{7}{10^3} + \frac{5}{10^4} = (.1875)_{\text{ten}}.$$

(a) Write the number $(.302)_{\text{four}}$ in the form of a rational number in base ten.
(b) Convert $(1.5)_{\text{ten}}$ to a representation in base four.
(c) Convert $(21.35)_{\text{ten}}$ to base five.
(d) Convert $(3.02)_{\text{four}}$ to base six.

3. Prove: There is no rational number x such that $x^2 = 3$.

4. Prove: There is no rational number x such that $x^3 = 2$.

5. Show that if n is a natural number, then $0 < 1/n \le 1$.

6. Show that if n is a natural number, then $0 < 1/n^2 \le 1/n$.

7. Consider the set T of positive rational numbers, with the ordering given by axioms O1 through O4.

(a) Prove that T is not well ordered; that is, there is a subset of T which does not have a least element.

(b) Are there rational numbers which are less than every element of T? Which of these is greatest?

(c) Define an ordering of T so that T is well ordered.

8. Using the division algorithm, develop the decimal representation of $\frac{1}{7}$.

9. Find the truth set of the sentence

$$(x - 1)(x + 1)(2x - 3)(x^2 - 2) = 0,$$

given that the domain of x is

(a) the set of natural numbers,   (b) the set of integers,
(c) the set of rational numbers,   (d) the set of real numbers.

10. Factor the polynomial $x^4 - 9$ into polynomials with coefficients
(a) in F,   (b) in R.

11. For the elements of the set T of positive rational numbers, let us define
a prime p to be a number in T, different from 1, that cannot be obtained as the
product of numbers in T that are all less than p. For example, $\frac{1}{3}$ is prime because if $ab = \frac{1}{3}$ and a, b are positive rational numbers, then either a or b is
greater than $\frac{1}{3}$. On the other hand, $\frac{4}{3}$ is composite, since $\frac{4}{3} = \frac{7}{6} \cdot \frac{8}{7}$ and $\frac{7}{6}, \frac{8}{7}$ are
each less than $\frac{4}{3}$. With this definition of a prime, show by a counterexample that
the positive rationals do not have the property of unique factorization.

12. (Continuation of problem 12 in Exercise Group 4–1 and problem 12 in
Exercise Group 4–2.) Continuing a construction of the number system from
the natural numbers, we extend the set of integers to the set of rational numbers
as follows.

Consider the set Q of all ordered pairs of integers:

$$(p, q) \text{ is an element of } Q \Leftrightarrow p, q \text{ are in } I, q \neq 0.$$

Define equality $\boxed{=}$, addition $\boxplus$, and multiplication $\boxed{\cdot}$ of elements of Q as follows. If (p, q) and (r, s) are in Q, then

$$(p, q) \boxed{=} (r, s) \Leftrightarrow ps = rq,$$
$$(p, q) \boxplus (r, q) \boxed{=} (p + r, q),$$
$$(p, q) \boxed{\cdot} (r, s) \boxed{=} (pr, qs).$$

First show that $\boxed{=}$ is an equivalence and the operations are well defined. Then:

(a) Prove: $(pa, qa) \boxed{=} (p, q)$ if $a \neq 0$.
(b) Prove: $(p, q) \boxplus (r, s) \boxed{=} (ps + qr, qs)$.
(c) Show that Q is closed under $\boxplus$ and $\boxed{\cdot}$.
(d) Show that $\boxplus$ and $\boxed{\cdot}$ are commutative and associative.
(e) Show that $\boxed{\cdot}$ is distributive through $\boxplus$.
(f) Show that $(0, q)$ is an identity for $\boxplus$; (q, q) is an identity for $\boxed{\cdot}$, for
any integer $q \neq 0$.
(g) Show that $(-p, q)$ is an additive inverse of (p, q).
(h) Show that (q, p) is a multiplicative inverse of (p, q), $p \neq 0$.
(i) Let Q_0 be the set of all equivalence classes in Q. If we define a mapping
f of Q_0 onto F by the correspondence

$$f: \text{ class } (pa, qa), \text{ for any } a \neq 0 \to \frac{p}{q},$$

show that f is a one-to-one mapping. In addition, show that under the mapping f, sums and products in Q_0 are paired with sums and products of corresponding elements in F. Then we say that Q_0 and F are isomorphic. We consider these two systems to be essentially the same, and we replace (pa, qa) by p/q whenever convenient.

(j) Consider the subset T of Q_0 consisting of all classes of elements of the form (rs, r) where r, s are in I, $r \neq 0$. Show that T is isomorphic to the set of integers I. (Define a one-to-one mapping f of T onto I for which f: $(rs, r) \rightarrow s$, and show that this mapping preserves sums and products.) In this sense, I is a subset of Q.

It is a significant fact in algebra that we may take any integral domain and apply the construction of this problem to form a field of elements (ordered pairs of elements of the integral domain) which has a subset isomorphic to the given integral domain. We say that any integral domain can be *embedded* in a field.

Chapter 5

The Real Numbers:
A Complete Ordered Field

5-1. LEAST UPPER BOUNDS AND THE COMPLETENESS AXIOM

Let us review the status of our axiomatic development of an abstract system whose model is the real number system. We assumed the existence of a set of elements which satisfy the axioms for an ordered field. Then we showed that the system of rational numbers is a model of this abstract system. On the other hand, we proved that the equation $x^2 = 2$ has no solution in the system of rational numbers, but we wish it to have a solution in the system of real numbers. We must conclude that our list of axioms for an ordered field does not entirely characterize the real numbers, for it fails to distinguish between rational and real numbers.

First, let us give intuitive reasons why we wish "$x^2 = 2$" to have a solution in the reals. Next, we state a final axiom and show that it implies the existence of real numbers that are not rational.

Throughout this development we made use of a number line to "picture" numbers as points. We used this device informally, assuming such ideas as "to the right," "distance," etc., without explicit definition. More rigorously we can define a mapping of F into the set of points on a line and show that this mapping is not onto, i.e., there are points on the line that cannot be paired with any rational numbers (even though F is a dense set). Our last objective is to show that the final axiom implies that there is a one-to-one mapping of R onto the set of all points of a line; thus, to each point there corresponds a real number, and to each real number there corresponds a point.

It is believed that "number" was first associated with *counting*, and later with *length*. The Greek mathematician Pythagoras reasoned that the length d of the diagonal of a square with side of length 1 satisfies the equation $d^2 = 2$. He concluded that there is a "number" d satisfying this equation because d represents a length. We could also reason that there is a point D on the line corresponding to the "number" d (Fig. 5–1). Similarly, we find a "number" π that measures the length of the segment between the beginning and ending points of tangency as a circle of unit diameter rolls through one revolution on a line (Fig. 5–2).

Pythagoras believed that all "numbers" were rational, the ratios of integers. When he finally proved that there is no rational number whose

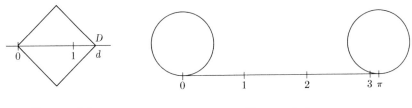

FIGURE 5–1   FIGURE 5–2

square is 2, he found himself in a dilemma. (Centuries later π was also proved to be not rational.)

This dilemma is resolved when we complete the description of the system of real numbers in such a way that all lengths of segments are associated with real numbers (in particular, so that $\sqrt{2}$ is a real number).

Before stating the axiom that will finish the description, we need the following definition.

Definition. A nonempty set S of real numbers is *bounded above* if there exists a real number M such that $s \leq M$ for every s in S. The number M is called an *upper bound* of S. A real number L is a *least upper bound* (lub) of S if

(a) L is an upper bound of S, and

(b) for every upper bound M of S, $L \leq M$.

For example, the finite set $T = \{1, 3, 5, 8, 17\}$ has 18 as an upper bound. In fact, any number 17 or greater serves as an upper bound of T. Obviously, the lub of T is 17. The infinite set

$$U = \left\{ \frac{1}{3}, \frac{2}{5}, \frac{3}{7}, \frac{4}{9}, \cdots, \frac{n}{2n+1}, \cdots \right\}$$

has $\frac{1}{2}$ as an upper bound, since

$$\frac{n}{2n+1} < \frac{1}{2} \qquad \text{for every } n \text{ in } N. \quad \text{(Prove this result.)}$$

It can also be shown that no real number c less than $\frac{1}{2}$ is an upper bound of U. Hence, the lub of U is $\frac{1}{2}$. In this case the lub of the set is not an element of the set. (Prove this result.)

If we restrict our attention to the set F of rational numbers, the question arises: does every bounded, nonempty subset of F have a least upper bound in F? Consider, for example, the set S of all positive rational numbers s such that $s^2 < 2$. This set is not empty, since 1 is in S, and it has an upper bound 2 in F ($s^2 < 2$ and $2 < 2^2 \Rightarrow s^2 < 2^2 \Rightarrow s < 2$). It will turn out that this bounded subset of F does *not* have a least upper bound in F.

Here we have the basic difference between the rationals and the reals. It is stated as our final axiom.

C (Completeness axiom). Every nonempty set of real numbers that has an upper bound in R has a least upper bound in R.

The least upper bound guaranteed by this axiom is *unique*. To show this, assume that the nonempty set S of real numbers is bounded above and has two least upper bounds L and L'. Then both L and L' are upper bounds of S. By definition, $L' \leq L$, since L' is a lub of S. For the same reason, $L \leq L'$. Hence, $L = L'$, and the lub of S is unique.

An ordered field whose elements satisfy axiom C is called a *complete ordered field*. We have finally obtained a satisfactory definition:

A real number is an element of a complete ordered field.

EXERCISE GROUP 5–1

1. Give two upper bounds and the lub of each of the following sets:

(a) $\left\{\dfrac{1}{2}, \dfrac{2}{3}, \dfrac{-3}{4}, \dfrac{5}{7}\right\}$ (b) $\{-3.6, \ -3.62, \ -3.615, \ -3.654\}$

2. Let T be the set of all real numbers t less than 1. Prove that 1 is the lub of T. (Assume that some real number c, $c < 1$, is an upper bound of T. Then apply the inequality

$$a < \frac{a + b}{2} < b$$

to c and 1, and show that there is a real number in T which is greater than c.)

3. Write corresponding definitions of a *lower bound* of a nonempty set and *greatest lower bound* (glb) of the set.

4. *Prove:* Every nonempty set of real numbers which has a lower bound in R has a glb in R. (Let s be any element of a nonempty set S with lower bound m; then

$$s \geq m \Rightarrow -s \leq -m.$$

Hence the set S' of all negatives $-s$ of elements of S has *upper bound* $-m$. Apply axiom C to S' to obtain the lub of S', say $-L$; then show that L must be the glb of S.)

5. Find upper and lower bounds of the following sets:

(a) $\left\{\dfrac{1}{2}, \dfrac{2}{3}, \dfrac{3}{4}, \ldots, \dfrac{n}{n+1}, \ldots\right\}$ (b) $\left\{\dfrac{1}{2}, \dfrac{2}{5}, \dfrac{3}{10}, \dfrac{4}{17}, \ldots, \dfrac{n}{n^2+1}, \ldots\right\}$

(c) $\left\{\dfrac{2}{1}, \dfrac{3}{2}, \dfrac{4}{3}, \ldots, \dfrac{n+1}{n}, \ldots\right\}$ (d) $\left\{\dfrac{2}{1}, \dfrac{5}{4}, \dfrac{10}{9}, \dfrac{17}{16}, \ldots, \dfrac{n^2+1}{n^2}, \ldots\right\}$

6. Find the lub of set (a) and the glb of each of (b), (c), and (d) in problem 5. Try to prove the results obtained.

For example, the glb of the set

$$\left\{ \frac{2}{1}, \frac{3}{2}, \frac{4}{3}, \ldots, \frac{n+1}{n}, \ldots \right\}$$

is 1. To prove this, we show that 1 is a lower bound of the set and that every number greater than 1 is not a lower bound. For every natural number n, $n + 1 > n$ (why?), and hence

$$\frac{n+1}{n} > 1;$$

that is, 1 is a lower bound of the set. Consider any number greater than 1, say $1 + e$, where e is an arbitrarily small positive real number (Fig. 5–3).

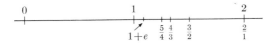

FIGURE 5–3

By means of the computation

$$\frac{n+1}{n} - 1 = \frac{1}{n} < e \Leftrightarrow n > \frac{1}{e},$$

we see that by choosing a natural number n_0 such that $n_0 > 1/e$,

$$n_0 > \frac{1}{e} \Rightarrow \frac{1}{n_0} < e \Rightarrow \frac{n_0 + 1}{n_0} - 1 < e \Rightarrow \frac{n_0 + 1}{n_0} < 1 + e;$$

that is, there is an element of the set, namely $(n_0 + 1)/n_0$, that is less than $1 + e$. Hence, 1 is the glb of the set. Note that we assumed intuitively the existence of a natural number greater than $1/e$. We shall prove this in the next section.

7. Prove that if an element of a set is an upper bound of the set, it must be the lub of the set.

8. Let a set S of real numbers have lub m and glb n.

(a) Let T be the set of all numbers of the form $s + 2$, where s is in S. What are the lub and glb of T? Prove your results.

(b) Let P be the set of all numbers of the form $-2s$, where s is in S. What are the lub and glb of P?

9. Let P, S be two sets of real numbers with lubs p and s, respectively. Consider the set $P + S$ consisting of all numbers $x + y$, where x is in P and y is in S, and the set $P \cup S$ consisting of all numbers belonging either to P or to S (the union of P with S). What are the lubs of $P + S$ and $P \cup S$?

5-2. $\sqrt{2}$ IS IN R

We know that the equation $x^2 = 2$ has no solution in F. It is our purpose in this section to show how the completeness axiom guarantees that $x^2 = 2$ *does* have a solution in R. An outline of the proof is as follows:

Consider the set T of all positive real numbers t such that $t^2 < 2$, and show that T has a lub, say x, in R. Then exactly one of the following sentences must be true:

$$x^2 < 2, \qquad x^2 > 2, \qquad \text{or} \qquad x^2 = 2.$$

If we can show that the first two cannot be true, we have the conclusion $x^2 = 2$.

In preparing the proof, we need three supporting theorems. The first says that for any two positive real numbers, there can be found a natural number multiple of one number which is greater than the other. This result is then used to prove the second and third. The second states that for any positive real number whose square is less than 2, there is a *greater* real number whose square is also less than 2. The third theorem asserts that for any positive real number whose square is greater than 2, there is a *lesser* positive real number whose square is also greater than 2. A moment of reflection will show that the second and third theorems, when proved, will rule out the possibilities of $x^2 < 2$ or $x^2 > 2$ if x is the lub of the set of positive real numbers whose squares are less than 2.

Theorem 5–1. For any two positive real numbers a and b, there is a natural number n such that $na > b$.

Proof by contradiction. For a given pair of positive real numbers a and b, assume that there is no n in N such that $na > b$. Then the set U of all products of the form na has the property that $na \le b$ for *every* n in N. Hence b is an upper bound of U. Now since U is nonempty, we know by axiom C that U has a lub in R, say c, such that every element of U is less than or equal to c. Since $n + 1$ is in N if n is in N, the number $(n + 1)a$ is in U. Then

$$(n + 1)a \le c,$$
$$na + a \le c,$$
$$na \le c - a \qquad \text{for every} \quad n \text{ in } N.$$

Thus $c - a$ is an *upper bound* of U. But $c - a < c$, since $a > 0$. Here we have a contradiction, for we cannot have an upper bound $c - a$ less than the lub c. Hence, the theorem is proved.

An ordered system that has the property of this theorem is called *Archimedean*.

For some purposes it is convenient to have an alternative statement of the Archimedean property:

> For any two positive real numbers a and b, there is a natural number n such that
>
> $$\frac{b}{n} < a.$$

We use this result to prove

Lemma 5–2. If a is any positive real number such that $a^2 < 2$, then there exists a real number b such that $b > a$ and $b^2 < 2$.

Proof. Given a in R, $a > 0$, $a^2 < 2$, let us construct the real number

$$b = a + \frac{a}{n},$$

where n is in N, and show that for some n

$$b > a \qquad \text{and} \qquad b^2 < 2.$$

For any n in N, $a + a/n > a$ (why?); hence $b > a$ for *every* n in N.

Now we compute, for any n in N,

$$b^2 = \left(a + \frac{a}{n}\right)^2 = a^2\left(1 + \frac{1}{n}\right)^2 \le a^2\left(1 + \frac{3}{n}\right).$$

Here the reader should pause and verify for himself that

$$\left(1 + \frac{1}{n}\right)^2 \le 1 + \frac{3}{n} \qquad \text{for every } n \text{ in } N.$$

Our proof will be finished if we can find some n such that

$$a^2\left(1 + \frac{3}{n}\right) < 2,$$

since for this n, $b^2 < 2$. In other words we must show that for some n,

$$1 + \frac{3}{n} < \frac{2}{a^2}, \qquad \text{that is,} \qquad \frac{3}{n} < \left(\frac{2}{a^2} - 1\right).$$

We know that 3 is positive, and we must show that $(2/a^2 - 1)$ is positive:

$$a^2 < 2 \Rightarrow \frac{2}{a^2} > 1 \Rightarrow \frac{2}{a^2} - 1 > 0.$$

Given these two positive numbers, the Archimedean property guarantees the existence of a natural number n such that

$$\frac{3}{n} < \left(\frac{2}{a^2} - 1\right).$$

For this n,

$$\frac{3}{n} + 1 < \frac{2}{a^2} \quad \text{and} \quad a^2\left(1 + \frac{3}{n}\right) < 2.$$

Combining these inequalities, we have for some n in N,

$$b^2 \le a^2\left(1 + \frac{3}{n}\right) \quad \text{and} \quad a^2\left(1 + \frac{3}{n}\right) < 2 \Rightarrow b^2 < 2.$$

This concludes the proof.

Lemma 5–3. If a is any positive real number such that $a^2 > 2$, then there exists a positive real number b such that $b < a$ and $b^2 > 2$.

Proof. Construct the real number

$$b = a - \frac{a}{n},$$

where n is in N, and show that for some n,

$$b > 0, \quad b < a, \quad b^2 > 2.$$

The reader can show that $b > 0$ and $b < a$ for any n in N, $n > 1$. Now compute

$$b^2 = \left(a - \frac{a}{n}\right)^2 = a^2\left(1 - \frac{1}{n}\right)^2 \ge a^2\left(1 - \frac{2}{n}\right).$$

We must find an n in N such that $a^2(1 - 2/n) > 2$, i.e.,

$$1 - \frac{2}{n} > \frac{2}{a^2}, \quad \text{that is,} \quad 1 - \frac{2}{a^2} > \frac{2}{n}.$$

Again, we use the Archimedean property. We know that 2 is positive and we show that $(1 - 2/a^2)$ is positive:

$$a^2 > 2 \Rightarrow \frac{2}{a^2} < 1 \Rightarrow 1 - \frac{2}{a^2} > 0.$$

Then there is some n in N such that

$$\frac{2}{n} < 1 - \frac{2}{a^2}.$$

For this n,

$$1 - \frac{2}{n} > \frac{2}{a^2} \quad \text{and} \quad a^2\left(1 - \frac{2}{n}\right) > 2.$$

By transitivity of inequalities, for some n in N,

$$b^2 \geq a^2 \left(1 - \frac{2}{n}\right) \quad \text{and} \quad a^2 \left(1 - \frac{2}{n}\right) > 2 \Rightarrow b^2 > 2,$$

and the lemma is proved.

The stage is now set for the main theorem of the section.

Theorem 5–4. (*Existence of $\sqrt{2}$ in R*). There is a positive real number x such that $x^2 = 2$.

Proof. Consider the set T of all positive real numbers t such that $t^2 < 2$. Certainly 1 is in T, since $1^2 < 2$; also

$$t^2 < 2 \text{ and } 2 < 2^2 \Rightarrow t^2 < 2^2 \Rightarrow t < 2,$$

and we see that 2 is an upper bound of T. Thus by axiom C the set T has a lub, say x. Now by O1 we are assured that exactly one of the following sentences is true:

$$x^2 < 2, \qquad x^2 > 2, \qquad x^2 = 2.$$

We shall rule out the first two as follows:

(1) Let x be the lub of T and assume that $x^2 < 2$. Then Lemma 5–2 asserts that there is a positive real number b such that

$$b > x \qquad \text{and} \qquad b^2 < 2.$$

Thus b is in T (since $b^2 < 2$). But this is a contradiction, for we cannot have any element of a set greater than its lub. Hence, "$x^2 < 2$" is false.

(2) Let x be the lub of T and assume that $x^2 > 2$. Then Lemma 5–3 exhibits a positive real number b such that

$$b < x \qquad \text{and} \qquad b^2 > 2.$$

Now for any element t of T, $t^2 < 2$, so that

$$t^2 < 2 \text{ and } 2 < b^2 \Rightarrow t^2 < b^2 \Rightarrow t < b.$$

Thus b is an upper bound of T. This is a contradiction, for b is less than the lub x. Hence "$x^2 > 2$" is false, and only the sentence "$x^2 = 2$" remains. This proves the theorem.

The reader may think that a great deal of effort has gone into a simple result. On the contrary, we have opened up a vast domain of new numbers.

It is now a simple matter to reword Lemmas 5–2, 5–3, and Theorem 5–4 by replacing the number 2 by *any* positive real number c. The result is

*Theorem 5–5. If c is any positive real number, then there is a unique positive real number x such that $x^2 = c$.

It is possible to go even further and prove that if c is any positive real number and n is any natural number, then there exists a positive real number x such that $x^n = c$.

Definition. If a is a positive real number, the unique *positive* solution of $x^2 = a$ is called the *square root* of a and is denoted by $\sqrt{a}$. The other solution of $x^2 = a$ is therefore $-\sqrt{a}$. In general, if a is a positive real number, the unique positive solution of $x^n = a$, n in N, is called the *n*th *root* of a and is denoted by $\sqrt[n]{a}$ ($\sqrt[n]{0} = 0$).

As a consequence of the above definition, we again have

$$\sqrt{a^2} = |a|.$$

For example,

$$\sqrt{(-3)^2} = |-3| = 3 \quad \text{and} \quad \sqrt{(x-1)^2} = |x-1|,$$

where the absolute-value notation guarantees that the square root is positive (or zero).

Real numbers that are not rational are called *irrational*. Thus $\sqrt{2}$ is an example of an irrational number. Not all irrational numbers are of the form $\sqrt[n]{a}$. Real numbers such as π, which are not solutions of polynomial equations, are also irrational.

EXERCISE GROUP 5–2

1. (a) *Prove:* There is a positive real number x such that $x^2 = 3$.

(b) Discuss the changes needed in Lemmas 5–2 and 5–3 and Theorem 5–4 to prove that there is a positive real number x such that

$$x^2 = c \quad \text{for any positive } c.$$

(c) *Prove:* If a is any positive real number such that $a^3 < 2$, then there exists a real number b such that

$$b > a \quad \text{and} \quad b^3 < 2.$$

(d) Outline a proof that there is a positive real number x such that $x^3 = 2$.

2. Find a positive rational number c such that $c > \frac{141}{100}$ and $c^2 < 2$.

3. Find a positive rational number d such that $d < \frac{142}{100}$ and $d^2 > 2$.

4. *Prove:* If a is in F and b is irrational, then

(a) $a + b$ is irrational   (b) ab is irrational, if $a \neq 0$ (c) $1/b$ is irrational.

5. *Prove:* The equation $x^2 + bx + c = 0$ (with b and c in R) has a solution in R if and only if $b^2 - 4c \geq 0$; there are one or two distinct solutions according as $b^2 - 4c = 0$ or $b^2 - 4c > 0$.

6. Prove the corollary to Theorem 5–1: For any two positive real numbers a and b, there is a natural number n such that

$$n > \frac{b}{a} \quad \text{and} \quad \frac{b}{n} < a.$$

7. Use the corollary in problem 6 to prove the existence of a natural number n such that $n > 1/e$ for any given positive e. (This proves a result assumed in problem 6, Exercise Group 5–1.)

5–3. CORRESPONDENCE BETWEEN *R* AND THE POINTS OF A LINE

In the previous section we found that the completeness axiom implies that certain numbers, such as $\sqrt{2}$, are in R although not in F. The completeness axiom implies more. It allows us to show that every point on the number line can be assigned a real number coordinate. This in turn will imply that to each line segment we may assign a real number which we call the measure of the length of the segment.

Just what do we mean by a number line and by the coordinate of a point on a number line? The reader certainly has formed an intuitive notion of a line as a certain infinite set of points. He also thinks, quite naturally, of an association between rational numbers and certain points of the line, an association in which the integers correspond to "equally spaced" points and the nonintegral rational numbers correspond to points between the integer points.

Our final theorem will state that to each point of the number line there corresponds exactly one real number (relative to a given correspondence between the rationals and certain points of the line). In the proof we shall refer to points to the "right" or "left" of a given point. Also, our discussion will assume the existence of a one-to-one mapping of F into the set of points of the line. The reader is probably willing to accept his natural instincts concerning "right" and "left" on the line and the definition of this mapping. Certainly we lean heavily on this intuition in teaching algebra.

Our intuition in these matters usually leads to correct results. Nonetheless, it may be worthwhile in the next few paragraphs to adopt some geometric language that could have the effect of minimizing our reliance on intuition.

Separation of a line. We say that if a point X is on a line, then X *separates* the line into two half-lines. If Y is another point on the line, then one of these half-lines contains Y and the other does not. If Z is in the half-line that does not contain Y, we say that X is *between* Y and Z. As

FIGURE 5-4

shown in Fig. 5–4, a *segment YZ* is the set of points on the line consisting of Y, Z and all points between Y and Z.

Rays. A point of a line, say X, together with a half-line determined by X, is called a *ray*. If Y is a point of this half-line, we indicate the ray by $\overrightarrow{XY}$. If Z is a point of the other half-line determined by X, we say that $\overrightarrow{XY}$ and $\overrightarrow{XZ}$ are rays with opposite *sense*. Two rays, $\overrightarrow{XY}$ and $\overrightarrow{UV}$, have the *same* sense if their intersection is also a ray. (Two rays of opposite sense intersect, if at all, in a point or a segment.)

The mapping f. Choose any two distinct points A, U on the line and define a mapping f of R into the set of points of the line as follows. Let f assign 0 to the point A, and 1 to the point U (Fig. 5–5). We shall say that point S is to the *right* of point T on the line if the ray $\overrightarrow{TS}$ has the same sense as the ray $\overrightarrow{AU}$; otherwise, S is to the *left* of T. (Note that "right" depends entirely on the choice of points A and U. For certain choices of A and U, "right" would coincide with our intuitive "left.")

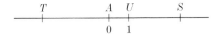

FIGURE 5-5

There is a point V on the line (Fig. 5–6) such that A bisects the segment VU; let f assign -1 to V. There is a point B such that U bisects AB; let f assign 2 to B. There is a point W such that V bisects WA; assign -2 to W. In this manner we successively assign each integer to a point of the line. As before, we call the number assigned by f to a point the *coordinate* of the point. (Strictly speaking, it is the *f-coordinate*, since the number assigned to a point depends on the mapping f.)

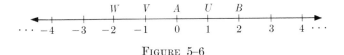

FIGURE 5-6

Similarly, let f assign $\frac{1}{2}$ to the midpoint of AU, $-\frac{1}{2}$ to the midpoint of VA, ..., $(2n + 1)/2$ to the midpoint of the segment joining points with the integer coordinates n and $n + 1$. We continue assigning rationals with denominators 3, 4, . . . until every rational is assigned. The reader can fill in the details; for example, let f assign $\frac{1}{3}$ and $\frac{2}{3}$ to the two trisection points of AU in such a way that the point corresponding to $\frac{1}{3}$ is between A and the point corresponding to $\frac{1}{2}$. At each stage the assignment is made in such a manner that for any three distinct points X, Y, Z with coordinates x, y, z, respectively,

$$Y \text{ is between } X \text{ and } Z \Leftrightarrow x < y < z \text{ or } z < y < x.$$

It then follows that Z is to the right of Y if and only if $z > y$.

We are now ready to show how the mapping f may be extended so that it assigns a real number to each point of the line.

Again, we need three preparatory theorems, each of which is used in the proof of the succeeding theorem.

Lemma 5–6. Given a nonempty set S of real numbers with lub x in R, if a is any number in R such that $a < x$, then there is a number b in S such that $b > a$.

DISCUSSION: It is instructive to view this lemma on the number line presented in Fig. 5–7, which shows that for any real number a less than the lub x of S (no matter how close a is to x), there is a number in S which is between a and x.

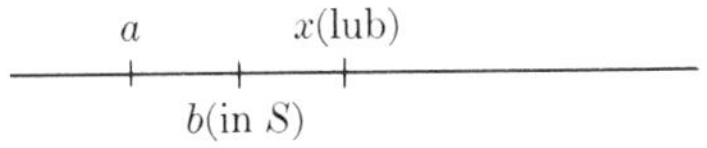

FIGURE 5–7

Proof by contradiction. Assume that there is no element of S greater than a. Then every element of S is less than or equal to a, and a is an upper bound of S. This is a contradiction, for $a < x$ and x is the lub of S. Hence, there is an element, say b, of S greater than a.

The following lemma is used to prove that each real number is a lub of a set of rational numbers.

Lemma 5–7. For a given number a in R, let S be the set of all rational numbers x such that $x < a$. Then a is the lub of S.

Proof. Since $x < a$ for all x in S, a is an upper bound of S. By axiom C we know that S has a lub, say y, such that $y \leq a$. If we can show that $y \not< a$, then $y = a$ and the lemma will be proved.

Assume that $y < a$, that is, $a - y > 0$. Then by Theorem 5–1 there is an n in N such that

$$\frac{1}{n} < a - y, \qquad y + \frac{1}{n} < a.$$

Also, $y - 1/n < y$. Now by Lemma 5–6 there is a z in S such that

$$y - \frac{1}{n} < z \quad \text{and} \quad z \leq y.$$

Then

$$y - \frac{1}{n} < z \leq y \Rightarrow y < z + \frac{1}{n} \leq y + \frac{1}{n} < a,$$

and

$$y < z + \frac{1}{n} < a.$$

This is a contradiction because $z + 1/n$ is in S (it is a rational number less than a) and cannot be greater than y, the lub of S. Hence "$y < a$" is false, and we have proved that $y = a$.

Note how the lemma looks on the number line (Fig. 5–8). If y is less than a, then there is some number $z + 1/n$ in S such that $z + 1/n > y$.

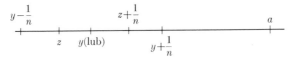

FIGURE 5–8

The final preparatory theorem states that between any two distinct real numbers there lies a rational number.

Theorem 5–8. If a and b are any two distinct real numbers such that $a < b$, then there is a *rational* number c such that $a < c < b$.

Proof. Let S be the set of all rational numbers x such that $x < b$. Then by the previous lemma, b is the lub of S. Now by Lemma 5–6

$$a < b \Rightarrow c > a \text{ for some } c \text{ in } S.$$

But if c is in S, then $c < b$. Hence,

$$a < c < b,$$

where c is a rational number.

Now we can prove the main theorem.

Theorem 5–9. Corresponding to each point P of the number line there is exactly one real number x.

Proof. Let P be a point on the number line to which no rational number has been assigned. We shall show that there is a unique real number x corresponding to P.

Let L be the set of all *rational* numbers corresponding to points to the *left* of P, and let R be the set of all *rational* numbers corresponding to points to the *right* of P. Now each rational number is in either L or R but not in both.

Let a be the lub of L and b the glb of R. Then exactly one of these sentences is true:

$$a < b, \qquad a > b, \qquad \text{or} \qquad a = b.$$

Assume that $a < b$. Then by Theorem 5–8 there is a *rational* number c such that $a < c < b$. Hence c, being rational, is in L or R, but not in both. This is a contradiction, for c cannot be in L (being greater than a) or in R (being less than b). Thus, $a \not< b$. Next assume that $a > b$. Then there is a rational number d such that $b < d < a$. Since d is rational and $d < a$ and $d > b$, we have d in both L and R, a contradiction. Hence, $a \not> b$, and we have shown that $a = b$. Since the lub of a set is unique, there is exactly one real number $x = a = b$ corresponding to P.

With this theorem we have finished the description of the system of real numbers as a *complete ordered field*. The consequences are far-reaching in many fields of mathematics, such as analytic geometry, calculus, and numerical analysis, to name only a few.

One of our original objectives is still not attained; we have no assurance that the equation $x^2 = a$, a in R, has a solution in R. (Only if $a \geq 0$ does it have a solution in R.) When one thinks of the great variety of algebraic equations that may be encountered, one might question whether we can ever develop a number system adequate to provide solutions for all algebraic equations. Fortunately, only one more extension is necessary, an extension to the *complex number system*, to guarantee all such solutions. This will be done in Chapter 8.

How may real numbers be represented? One of the consequences of the theorems in this section is the fact (see problem 4) that a given irrational number may be approximated as closely as desired by a rational number. A discussion of representation is given in Chapter 6.

IMPLICATIONS. How much of the theory of this chapter should be included in a high-school algebra course? It is not reasonable to expect that many students would understand the details of this development if it were included in an elementary course. The purpose of the present chapter is to give *the teacher* a clear understanding of the nature and character of the real number system. Only then can he transmit to his students a correct intuitive picture of the distinction between rationals and irrationals.

There are various models of an ordered field, such as $(F, +, \cdot)$ and $(R, +, \cdot)$, but there is only one model of a complete ordered field, namely, the real numbers. (By this we mean that any two models are isomorphic to each other, having precisely the same structure.) It may not be advisable to speak even of fields in a first course in algebra. Certainly there should be major emphasis on the properties of an ordered field, even though this terminology is not used. For example, a student can be led to discover that the operations of addition and multiplication have properties, here designated by F1 through F7 and O1 through O4, and that these properties are basic to all that he does with or understands about numbers and the symbols he uses for numbers. In a second course in algebra, he can understand that some real numbers are not rational and that the reals must have some property not shared by the rationals. His exposure to high-school algebra could very well culminate in a listing of these basic properties, including that of completeness. Then examples of mathematical systems having some of these properties and not others would give him a larger perspective of what algebra means in terms of the studies of mathematical systems.

EXERCISE GROUP 5–3

1. Prove the counterpart of Lemma 5–6: Given a nonempty set T of real numbers with glb y in R. If b is any real number such that $b > y$, then there is a number c in T such that $c < b$.

2. Prove the counterpart of Lemma 5–7: For a given b in R, let T be the set of all rational numbers y such that $y > b$. Then b is the glb of T.

3. Prove the statement made in Section 5–1: The set S of all rational numbers s such that $s^2 < 2$ does not have a lub in F. (Between the real numbers a and $\sqrt{2}$, $a < \sqrt{2}$, there is a rational number, by Theorem 5–8.)

4. *Prove:* If ϵ is any given arbitrarily small positive real number and a is any given real number, then there is a rational number x such that $|x - a| < \epsilon$. (That is, any real number can be approximated as closely as desired by a rational number. Since $a - \epsilon < a + \epsilon$, then between $a - \epsilon$ and $a + \epsilon$ there is a rational number, by Theorem 5–8.)

5. For each n in N, let I_n be the set of numbers x satisfying

$$a_n \leq x \leq b_n, \qquad a_n < b_n.$$

(I_n is called an *interval* and is sometimes written $[a_n, b_n]$.)
    If

$$a_n \leq a_{n+1}, \qquad b_{n+1} \leq b_n,$$

and if

$$b_n - a_n = \frac{1}{10^n},$$

then the set $\{I_1, I_2, \ldots, I_n, \ldots\}$ is called a *nest of intervals*. Note that $I_1 \supset I_2 \supset I_3 \supset \cdots$ Prove that under these conditions there is *exactly one* real number which is in *every* I_n. (Show that the set $\{a_1, a_2, \ldots, a_n, \ldots\}$ is bounded above and hence has a unique lub a. Then show that a is in every I_n. Finally, show that if c is in every I_n and $c \neq a$, there is a contradiction.)

6. Which of the ordered systems

$$(N, +, \cdot), \qquad (I, +, \cdot), \qquad (F, +, \cdot), \qquad \text{and} \quad (R, +, \cdot)$$

are complete? (Either prove completeness or give a counterexample.)

7. (Continuation of problem 12 in Exercise Group 4–1, problem 12 in Exercise Group 4–2, and problem 12 in Exercise Group 4–3.) In the alternative process of constructing the real number system from the natural numbers, we extended the natural numbers to the integers, then the integers to the rational numbers. We accomplished each extension by considering the set of all ordered pairs of elements from the preceding system and defining equality, addition, and multiplication of these pairs in appropriate ways. At each step, the extended system contained a subsystem isomorphic to the preceding system.

It would be natural to attempt a similar extension from the system of rationals to the system of reals. Unfortunately, such an extension is not quite as simple as it was before. Instead of constructing all ordered pairs of rational numbers, we consider the set of all regular sequences of rational numbers.

A *sequence* is an infinite ordered set $a_1, a_2, a_3, \ldots$, denoted by $\{a_i\}$. A *regular* (*Cauchy*) sequence is one with the property that for each real $e > 0$, there is a natural number k such that

$$n > k \text{ and } m > k \Rightarrow |a_n - a_m| < e.$$

This is a careful way of saying that no matter how small a number e we specify, there is a position in the sequence beyond which every pair of elements of the sequence differs by a number less than e.

Let us denote by V the set of all regular sequences of rational numbers:

$\{a_i\}$ is an element of $V \Leftrightarrow \{a_i\}$ is regular and a_i is in F for all i in N.

For $\{a_i\}$, $\{b_i\}$ in V define equality, addition, and multiplication by:

$\{a_i\} = \{b_i\} \Leftrightarrow$ for each $e > 0$ there is a k in N such that

$$i > k \Leftrightarrow |a_i - b_i| < e.$$

$\{a_i\} + \{b_i\} = \{(a_i + b_i)\}.$

$\{a_i\} \cdot \{b_i\} = \{a_i b_i\}.$

First verify that $=$ is an equivalence in V. Then:

(a) Show that V is closed under $+$; that is, show that $\{(a_i + b_i)\}$ is a regular sequence if $\{a_i\}$ and $\{b_i\}$ are regular.

(b) Show that V is closed under $\cdot$.

It can be proved that a sequence of rationals is regular if and only if it converges to a limit* which is a real number and is unique. Thus there is a one-to-one correspondence between the set of classes of regular sequences of rational numbers and the set of real numbers. This correspondence preserves operations, so that $(V, +, \cdot)$ is isomorphic to $(R, +, \cdot)$. *Note for part (b):* We need the fact that if $\{a_i\}$ is regular, then there is a positive M such that $|a_i| < M$ for all i; that is, $\{a_i\}$ is *bounded*. Try to prove this fact. Then write

$$|a_n b_n - a_m b_m| \leq |a_n| \, |b_n - b_m| + |b_m| \, |a_n - a_m|, \quad \text{etc.}$$

REMARK. There are two alternative, and complementing, ways of approach to a definition of the real number system. Teachers of algebra should be aware of these alternatives and the contribution each might make to the student's understanding of real numbers.

(1) We can follow the development of Chapters 3 and 5 in which we state axioms for a complete ordered field, and then assume the existence of a system satisfying these axioms and call it the real number system. Then we study the properties of the various subsystems, as we did in Chapter 4.

(2) We can begin by assuming the existence of the natural numbers, a set satisfying certain axioms such as Peano's axioms. Then we construct from this set the system of integers; from this the system of rationals; and from this the system of reals. The successive constructions are described in a series of problems: 12 in Exercise Group 4–1, 12 in Exercise Group 4–2, 12 in Exercise Group 4–3, and 7 in Exercise Group 5–3. At each stage of construction the properties of the system can be proved as consequences of the construction.

Each of these alternative descriptions of the real number system has its advantages and disadvantages. The first (presented in the text) is somewhat simpler to develop and requires less mathematical background. The second (described in the problems) more closely parallels the historical development of real numbers and builds on a minimal number of axioms. Undoubtedly the second approach requires more mathematical sophistication than most students have, but any student who aspires to a career in mathematics must some day understand both alternatives and see that each is a description of the same system.

---

* See, for example, Walter Rudin, *Principles of Mathematical Analysis*, McGraw-Hill, 1953, pp. 39 and 40.

Chapter 6

Decimal Representation of Real Numbers

6–1. INFINITE DECIMALS

It was established in Chapter 4 that integers and rational numbers may be represented by decimals, the integers always terminating and the rational numbers sometimes nonterminating (*infinite*). It was also shown that if a rational number has an infinite decimal representation, it is *periodic* in the sense that its digits repeat in a regular fashion. This leaves unanswered the question, is every periodic decimal the representation of a rational number? After we answer this in the affirmative, a new question is raised: what numbers, if any, are represented by nonperiodic infinite decimals?

We know that a positive number x is *represented* by an infinite decimal x if x satisfies *every* one of the inequalities in the infinite set of inequalities:

$$a_k \leq x \leq b_k, \qquad a_k < b_k, \qquad b_k - a_k = \frac{1}{10^k}, \qquad k = 1, 2, 3, \ldots,$$

where

$$a_k = c_n 10^n + \cdots + c_0 + \frac{d_1}{10} + \cdots + \frac{d_k}{10^k},$$

$$b_k = c_n 10^n + \cdots + c_0 + \frac{d_1}{10} + \cdots + \frac{d_k + 1}{10^k},$$

n is in N, and each c_i and d_i is some integer in $\{0, 1, \ldots, 9\}$. Then we write $x = c_n \ldots c_0.d_1 \ldots d_k \ldots$

We shall show that *all real numbers have decimal representations* and *every decimal represents a unique real number*. Then, if a real number is *not* rational, its decimal representation is *not* periodic. Conversely, since every rational number is represented by a terminating or a periodic decimal, it follows that if a decimal is neither terminating nor periodic it must represent a real number which is not rational. Here we have another distinction between rational and irrational numbers—a distinction of *periodicity* of their decimal representations.

The above remarks need to be verified. First, let us show that all decimals represent real numbers. Of course, if a decimal terminates, then by definition it is the *rational* sum of a finite set of rational numbers, each of the form

$$c_i 10^i \quad \text{or} \quad \frac{d_i}{10^i}, \qquad 0 \le c_i \le 9, \qquad 0 \le d_i \le 9.$$

Thus it is sufficient to show that all infinite decimals represent real numbers. For example, consider the infinite decimal

$$.232332333233332\ldots$$

and the corresponding infinite set of terminating decimals

$$D = \{.2, .23, .232, .2323, .23233, .232332, .2323323, \ldots\},$$

where each terminating decimal in D contains one more digit than the preceding one had. Certainly D is a nonempty set of rational numbers which has an upper bound, say 1. Hence, by axiom C, D has a *unique least upper bound which is a real number.* We shall show that this unique lub of D is the unique real number represented by the infinite decimal .2323323332.... Consider the infinite set of inequalities:

$$a_1 = .2 \quad < .3 \quad = b_1,$$
$$a_2 = .23 \quad < .24 \quad = b_2,$$
$$a_3 = .232 < .233 = b_3,$$

$$\text{etc.}$$

Since $a_n < b_n$, $a_n \le a_{n+1}$, $b_{n+1} \le b_n$, and $b_n - a_n = 1/10^n$ for all n in N, there is exactly one real number which satisfies every inequality, and this number is the lub of D. (See problem 5 in Exercise Group 5–3.) In general, corresponding to each infinite decimal $.d_1 d_2 \ldots d_k \ldots$, there is an infinite set of terminating decimals

$$D = \{.d_1, .d_1 d_2, .d_1 d_2 d_3, \ldots, .d_1 d_2 \ldots d_k, \ldots\},$$

$0 \le d_i \le 9$, which is bounded above and has a lub which is the unique real number represented by the infinite decimal.

   Conversely, every real number can be represented by a decimal. This has been shown for rationals; it remains to be shown for irrationals. We first recall that any irrational number may be approximated as closely as desired by a rational number (see problem 4 in Exercise Group 5–3). For our purposes let us state this fact in the following form: Given any irrational number y and any positive rational number e, no matter how small, there is a rational number x such that

$$y - e < x < y, \quad \text{that is,} \quad x < y < x + e.$$

Now it is possible to generate a set of successive rational approximations a_k to y corresponding to the successive values of e: 1, .1, .01, .001, ... Hence, we have a set of inequalities

$$a_0 < y < a_0 + 1 \quad = b_0,$$

$$a_1 < y < a_1 + \frac{1}{10} \ = b_1,$$

$$a_2 < y < a_2 + \frac{1}{10^2} = b_2,$$

etc.

and for *every* k in N,

$$a_k < y < a_k + \frac{1}{10^k} = b_k,$$

where $a_k < b_k$, $a_k \le a_{k+1}$, $b_{k+1} \le b_k$, $b_k - a_k = 1/10^k$. This set of rational approximations a_k will be bounded above and will have y as its lub. The corresponding infinite decimal will represent y.

For example, let us find the infinite decimal representation of the irrational number $\sqrt{2}$. Corresponding to $e = 1$,

$$1 < \sqrt{2} < 1 + 1, \quad \text{since } 1 < 2 < 4.$$

Corresponding to $e = .1$,

$$1.4 \quad < \sqrt{2} < 1.4 \quad + .1, \quad \text{since } (1.4)^2 \quad < 2 < (1.5)^2;$$

$$e = .01: \ 1.41 \ < \sqrt{2} < 1.41 \ + .01, \quad \text{since } (1.41)^2 \ < 2 < (1.42)^2;$$

$$e = .001: 1.414 < \sqrt{2} < 1.414 + .001, \quad \text{since } (1.414)^2 < 2 < (1.415)^2;$$

etc.

The lub of the set $\{1, 1.4, 1.41, 1.414, \ldots\}$ is the irrational number $\sqrt{2}$, and is represented by the infinite decimal 1.414...

It is not surprising that the completeness axiom provides the answer to the problem of decimal representation of real numbers. After all, it is this axiom which finishes the characterization of R. However, it must be noted that we have stated an *existence* theorem for decimal representation of an irrational number. It tells us that there *is* a decimal, but it does not spell out a method for finding the particular digits of the decimal. For square roots there are algorithms of various types which exhibit the digits of the representation, but for such irrational numbers as π, e, $\log 2$, etc., we must develop special methods for each number.

Now we are assured that any infinite decimal, say

$$.3212121... = .3\dot{2}\dot{1},$$

represents a real number. It remains to show that *it is a rational number if its representation is periodic*. To illustrate the technique that we shall use, let us consider the periodic decimal $.3\dot{2}\dot{1}$. Let $.212121\ldots$ represent a real number N so that

$$.3212121\ldots = \frac{3}{10} + \frac{N}{10}.$$

Now

$$N = .2121\ldots \Rightarrow 100N = 21.2121\ldots$$
$$\Rightarrow 100N = 21 + N$$
$$\Rightarrow \quad 99N = 21$$
$$\Rightarrow \quad N = \tfrac{7}{33}.$$

Hence,

$$.3212121\ldots = \tfrac{3}{10} + \tfrac{7}{330} = \tfrac{53}{165},$$

which is a rational number. Long division will verify the periodicity.

It is interesting to study the decimal $.999\ldots9\ldots = .\dot{9}$. If $N = .999\ldots$, then $10N = 9.999\ldots = 9 + N$. Hence, $9N = 9$ and $N = 1$. Thus we see that the rational number 1 can be represented by either $1.000\ldots$ or by $.999\ldots$. This choice of two periodic decimal representations is possible for every terminating decimal:

$$.325 = .325000\ldots = .324999\ldots = .324\dot{9},$$
$$4.728 = 4.728\dot{0} = 4.727\dot{9}.$$

The technique used above can be applied to any periodic decimal as follows. Let us assume that the repeating block of k digits first occurs after the jth digit to the right of the decimal point.

$$x = c_n c_{n-1} \ldots c_1 c_0 . d_1 d_2 \ldots d_j \underbrace{\dot{d}_{j+1} d_{j+2} \ldots \dot{d}_{j+k}}_{k \text{ digits}}.$$

Then x is the sum of a rational terminating decimal and a periodic decimal:

$$x = c_n c_{n-1} \ldots c_1 c_0 . d_1 d_2 \ldots d_j + \frac{1}{10^j} (.\dot{d}_{j+1} d_{j+2} \ldots \dot{d}_{j+k}).$$

Let $.\dot{d}_{j+1} d_{j+2} \ldots \dot{d}_{j+k}$ represent a real number N. Then

$$10^k N = d_{j+1} d_{j+2} \ldots d_{j+k} . \dot{d}_{j+1} d_{j+2} \ldots \dot{d}_{j+k},$$
$$10^k N = d_{j+1} d_{j+2} \ldots d_{j+k} + N,$$
$$N = \frac{d_{j+1} d_{j+2} \ldots d_{j+k}}{10^k - 1}.$$

Thus N is a rational number since it is the quotient of the integers represented by $d_{j+1} d_{j+2} \ldots d_{j+k}$ and $10^k - 1$. Hence, x is a rational number.

To summarize, these are the facts we have learned:

(1) Every decimal represents a unique real number.

(2) Every real number has a decimal representation.

(3) The infinite decimal $.d_1d_2 \ldots d_k \ldots$ represents the lub of the infinite set D of rational numbers:

$$D = \{.d_1, .d_1d_2, .d_1d_2d_3, \ldots, .d_1d_2 \ldots d_k, \ldots\}$$

(4) The decimal representation of a real number is *periodic* if and only if it is a *rational* number (terminating decimals may be considered as periodic decimals with repeating zeros).

(5) The representation of a real number is *nonperiodic* if and only if it is an *irrational* number.

6–2. R IS NOT COUNTABLE

Since we know that all real numbers can be represented as infinite decimals, we are in a position to prove a statement made in Chapter 4: The set R is not countable. For simplicity, let us restrict our attention to the set Q of all real numbers x such that $0 < x < 1$. If we can prove that this set is not countable, then certainly R is not countable.

Let us assume the negative, namely, that the set Q of all real numbers between 0 and 1 is countable, and obtain a contradiction. This means that we assume there is a one-to-one mapping f of N onto Q. Every real number in Q can be written as an infinite decimal, where we may agree to write terminating decimals as periodic decimals with repeating zeros. Then under the mapping f, each element of Q is paired with one element of N:

$$
\begin{array}{cl}
\underline{N} & \underline{Q} \\
1 & \leftrightarrow .a_1a_2a_3 \ldots a_k \ldots \\
2 & \leftrightarrow .b_1b_2b_3 \ldots b_k \ldots \\
3 & \leftrightarrow .c_1c_2c_3 \ldots c_k \ldots \\
\vdots & \qquad \vdots \\
n & \leftrightarrow .r_1r_2r_3 \ldots r_k \ldots \\
\vdots & \qquad \vdots
\end{array}
$$

where all the digits are in the set $\{0, 1, 2, \ldots, 9\}$. Since f is an onto mapping, every real number in Q is in this list. To show a contradiction, let us construct a real number x in Q which *cannot* be listed. Form

$$x = .t_1t_2t_3 \ldots t_k \ldots,$$

with none of its digits 9, where t_1 is a digit different from a_1, t_2 is different from b_2, t_3 is different from c_3, $\ldots$, t_n is different from r_n, $\ldots$ Certainly

x is different from each real number listed because it differs in at least one digit from each of the numbers. Yet x must be in Q because it is represented by a positive decimal which is less than 1. This is a contradiction; hence R is not countable.

EXERCISE GROUP 6-2

1. Find the rational number represented by each of the following periodic decimals.

(a) .$1\dot{2}\dot{3}$ (b) $4.3\dot{1}$ (c) .$00\dot{3}\dot{6}$

(d) .$1\dot{4}285\dot{7}$ (e) $6.35\dot{0}$ (f) .$10\dot{9}$

2. Determine the first four elements of an infinite set of terminating decimals whose lub is:

(a) $\sqrt{3}$ (b) $\frac{1}{3}$ (c) $\sqrt[3]{2}$ (d) $\sqrt{5}$

3. Find a terminating decimal:

(a) between $\sqrt{5}$ and $\sqrt{6}$ [*Hint:* $\sqrt{5} < t < \sqrt{6} \Leftrightarrow 5 < t^2 < 6$.]

(b) between $\sqrt{43}$ and $\sqrt{44}$

(c) between $\frac{31}{33}$ and $\frac{32}{33}$

4. Prove that the infinite decimal

$$.101001000100001000001\ldots,$$

where the number of 0's between successive 1's increases as indicated, represents an irrational number.

5. Explain why neither 3.1416 nor $\frac{22}{7}$ represents the number π.

6. A real number may be represented by an infinite set of digits taken from any set of integers of the form $\{0, 1, \ldots, (k-1)\}$. For example, if $k = 2$, we have *binary* representation. Then

$$10.11_{\text{two}} = 1 \cdot 2 + 0 \cdot 1 + \frac{1}{2} + \frac{1}{2^2}.$$

Find the rational numbers in the binary scale represented by each of the following periodic binary forms.

(a) .$\dot{1}$ (b) .$0\dot{1}$ (c) .$1\dot{1}\dot{0}$ (d) $1.0\dot{1}0\dot{1}$

Chapter 7

Algebraic Expressions and Functions

7–1. WHAT IS A VARIABLE?

In a study of the real number system, we make statements such as:

(1) For any a and b in R, $a + b = b + a$.

In an algebra course we write statements such as the formal equation

$$(2) \qquad \frac{x^2 - 4}{x + 2} = x - 2.$$

In the sentences above there occur symbols such as a, b, and x and other symbols such as 2 and 4; the latter two are called numerals because they represent specific numbers. We usually call symbols such as a, b, and x *variables*, using the word loosely. It is not at all clear that variables play the same role in sentences (1) and (2). In the first statement a and b may represent any elements in R; in this context a *variable represents one element of a given set*, although the element is not specified. Thus, (1) says that regardless of which numbers in R are represented by a and b, $a + b$ and $b + a$ represent the same number in R.

In the second statement we have nothing so definite for a meaning of x because there is no indication that x represents anything at all. There is no doubt that (2) was suggested in the first place by relations among numbers, but as it stands here it is a statement of the equivalence of two formal expressions,

$$\frac{x^2 - 4}{x + 2} \qquad \text{and} \qquad x - 2,$$

obtained by some rules of operations on such expressions. In this context, a *variable is an indeterminate*, a symbol whose meaning has not been specified.

This second type of variable takes on the same character as the first type as soon as we require that x represent a number from a given set of numbers. Until such a requirement is made, x is nothing more than a symbol which helps to hold the form of the expression in which it occurs.

One's first reaction is that confusion between these two types of variables could be avoided by the simple device of never considering the second type. This alternative is probably a good one to use in a beginning algebra course, but sooner or later a student finds out that mathematicians sometimes treat variables as indeterminates, and for very good reasons.

A teacher may (and probably should) present algebra to beginners in such a way that every bit of manipulation of expressions is a consequence of the properties of real numbers. In such an approach there is no rote "symbol pushing," since every symbol is a numeral for a real number and hence is governed by well-established properties of real numbers. However, the teacher should be aware of the possibility of treating algebraic expressions themselves as elements of a system, whether or not they represent numbers.

7–2. ALGEBRA OF EXPRESSIONS

Refer again to sentence (1) of the preceding section and forget for the moment that the statement concerns real numbers. Then the commutative property becomes a rule for transforming expressions; that is, $a + b$ and $b + a$ are "equal" expressions. From this point of view the various properties listed in F1 through F7 constitute a set of rules for transforming expressions. Attention is thus shifted from the system of real numbers to the *symbols* used to describe them. We are now concerned with the *form* of the expression rather than with the number it represents. Thus, we manipulate expressions with reference to a system of expressions. Let us describe this system carefully.

Consider any set S of numerals and the set of four binary connectives $+$, $-$, $\times$, $\div$. The numerals in S may represent any subset of R (or possibly the set of complex numbers). Now let us attach to the set S any indeterminate symbols, say x, y, z, a, b, c, ... From the enlarged set we construct algebraic expressions over the set represented by S as follows.

Definition.

(1) Each of the indeterminates and numerals is an algebraic expression. For example, x, 3 are algebraic expressions.

(2) Given any two algebraic expressions A and B and a connective $*$ from the set of connectives, then $A * B$ is an algebraic expression. For example, $x + 3$ is an algebraic expression.

(3) If A is an algebraic expression, then $\sqrt[n]{A}$ is an algebraic expression, where n represents an element in N. For example, $\sqrt[3]{x + 3}$ is an algebraic expression.

(4) Any finite number of applications of (1), (2), or (3) results in an algebraic expression. For example, $x\sqrt[3]{x + 3} + 3(x + 3)$ is an algebraic expression.

Thus algebraic expressions over a set are those which can be constructed from indeterminates and numerals for elements of the set by the above rules of formation, somewhat in the same manner that English expressions are formed from words by certain rules of grammar. For example,

$$\frac{\sqrt[4]{x - y}}{2x + 3}$$

is an algebraic expression* over I. (The reader can verify this by tracing the sequence of operations which generates the expression from the symbols x, y and numerals representing elements of I.) On the other hand,

$$\frac{\sqrt[+]{x -}}{+3}$$

is not an algebraic expression because it does not conform to prescribed mathematical "grammar," whereas

$$\sin x$$

is not an algebraic expression because it requires an *infinite* sequence of permissible operations for its representation:†

$$\sin x = x - \frac{x^3}{3!} + \frac{x^5}{5!} - \frac{x^7}{7!} + \cdots$$

Now consider the system of all algebraic expressions over the set R of all real numbers and the binary operations of indicated addition and multiplication. By definition, to each element A of this system there corresponds an element $(-1)A$ and an element $1 \div A$ in the system. Let us agree to abbreviate "$(-1)A$" to "$-A$" and "$1 \div A$" to "$1/A$."

We are now in a familiar position. We have a system of elements (expressions) and two binary operations (indicated addition and multiplication) such that for any two elements A, B of the system, $A + B$ and AB are unique elements of the system. How shall we define equality for expressions? We go back to the first meaning of the variables and agree that the expressions A and B are "equal" provided that for each permissible value of each variable involved in A and B the numerals A and B name the same number. For example,

$$x^2 - 1 = (x + 1)(x - 1)$$

---

* We agree that "$A \div B$" may be written "$\dfrac{A}{B}$."

† See George B. Thomas, *Calculus and Analytic Geometry*, Addison-Wesley, Reading, Mass., p. 798.

because for each value of x (as a real number), the phrases $x^2 - 1$ and $(x + 1)(x - 1)$ are numerals for the same real number.

The numerals 0 and 1 are themselves expressions and serve as the additive and multiplicative identities in the system of expressions. For example, the expression $x(x - 1) - x^2 + x$ is the zero expression, since it has the value zero for each real value of x.

Given this definition of equality, the system of expressions has the following properties:

(1) If A, B are expressions, then $A + B = B + A$, $AB = BA$.

(2) If A, B, C are expressions, then $(A + B) + C = A + (B + C)$, $(AB)C = A(BC)$.

(3) If A, B, C are expressions, then $A(B + C) = AB + AC$.

(4) There is an expression 0 such that $A + 0 = A$ for every expression A.

(5) There is an expression $1(\neq 0)$ such that $A \cdot 1 = A$ for every expression A.

(6) For each expression A there is an expression $-A$ such that $A + (-A) = 0$.

(7) For each expression $A \neq 0$ there is an expression $\dfrac{1}{A}$ such that $A\dfrac{1}{A} = 1$.

Hence the system of algebraic expressions is a field. With this fact established we have a list of ready-made theorems concerning operations on elements in this system. These are the theorems derived from the field axioms in Chapter 3, with "element of $\mathfrak{F}$" replaced by "algebraic expression."

Thus we may study operations on algebraic expressions independent of their connection with real numbers. Work in factoring, simplification of expressions, division of polynomials, etc., forms a small part of the study of this system. This way of looking at the language of algebra is implicit in much of a beginning course and turns up explicitly in later courses. A good student automatically shifts to this point of view about algebraic manipulations as he matures. However, if this occurs before he understands that an algebraic system underlies his manipulations, there is danger of confusion. For this reason it has been suggested that in a beginning course only the first meaning of a variable be used.

Just as the system of real numbers has interesting subsystems, so has the system of algebraic expressions over a set S.

Definition. The subsystem of algebraic expressions over S obtained by applying only (1), (2), and (4) of the previous definition is called the system of *rational expressions* over S.

For example,*

$$\frac{3x^3a \,-\, xy}{\sqrt{2} \,-\, x} \quad \text{and} \quad 5xy \,-\, a^2b \,+\, \pi$$

are rational expressions over R, whereas

$$\frac{3ab}{\sqrt{x \,-\, a}}$$

is an algebraic expression over I which is *not* rational because it involves operation (3) of extracting a root.

Definition. The subsystem of rational expressions over S obtained by using only the subset of connectives $+$, $-$, $\times$ is called the system of *polynomials* over S. A *monomial* is a polynomial obtained by using only the connective $\times$.

For example,

$$3x^2a \,-\, 4yb \text{ is a polynomial over } I,$$

$$\frac{4x}{5} + \frac{3a^2bc}{4} \text{ is a polynomial}\dagger \text{ over } F, \text{ and}$$

$$\sqrt{2}\,x^2 \,-\, 5 \text{ is a polynomial over } R.$$

Of special interest are polynomials in one indeterminate over R. These are of the form

$$a_0 + a_1x + a_2x^2 + \cdots + a_nx^n,$$

where $a_0, a_1, \ldots, a_n$ represent elements in R, $a_n \neq 0$ when n is a positive integer, and $a_0 \neq 0$ or $a_0 = 0$ when $n = 0$. A good deal of attention is given to such polynomials in a first course of algebra. A student learns to add and multiply polynomials, making use of associative, commutative, and distributive properties. When he learns to factor polynomials (that is, into products of polynomials), he finds that he must be careful to specify the set over which the factorization takes place. For example, the polynomial over F,

$$x^2 \,-\, \tfrac{1}{4},$$

is not factorable into polynomials over I, but is factorable over F; whereas the polynomial over I,

$$x^2 \,-\, 2,$$

_____

* Note that $\sqrt{2}$ is an element of R and is not thought of as requiring operation (3) of the definition.

† The rational numbers $\frac{4}{5}$ and $\frac{3}{4}$ are *multiplied* by other expressions, and no division is involved.

is factorable into polynomials over R but not over F or I. To illustrate the necessity of specifying the set over which factorization takes place, let us find the factors of the polynomial

$$x^4 - \tfrac{1}{9}.$$

(a) It is not factorable over I.

(b) Its factors over F are $(x^2 - \tfrac{1}{3})(x^2 + \tfrac{1}{3})$.

(c) Its factors over R are $(x - \sqrt{\tfrac{1}{3}})(x + \sqrt{\tfrac{1}{3}})(x^2 + \tfrac{1}{3})$.

(d) Its factors over the set of complex numbers are

$$(x - \sqrt{\tfrac{1}{3}})(x + \sqrt{\tfrac{1}{3}})(x - i\sqrt{\tfrac{1}{3}})(x + i\sqrt{\tfrac{1}{3}}).$$

As a student studies polynomials, he notices their similarity to integers. Like the integers, the set of polynomials is closed under addition, subtraction, and multiplication, but not under division; and also like integers, they have the property of unique prime factorization over a given set. This suggests why some writers call polynomials *integral expressions*.

If A and B are polynomials over S, then their quotient A/B is certainly a rational expression over S. Conversely, it can also be shown that every rational expression over S can be represented as the quotient of two polynomials over S. The analogy with rational numbers suggests the adjective "rational" for such expressions.

The reader should verify that the system of polynomials in one variable over R is a ring, and that the system of rational expressions in one variable over R is a field.

EXERCISE GROUP 7–2

1. Identify each of the following expressions over S as polynomial, rational, algebraic, and specify the set S.

(a) $\sqrt{5x} - y + a - 2$

(b) $\dfrac{\pi}{3} y - \dfrac{9x}{\dfrac{x - 2}{y - 2}}$

(c) $\dfrac{|3 - x|}{4x}$

(d) $\dfrac{3}{x} + \sqrt{\dfrac{y}{2}}$

(e) $\dfrac{1}{3} - \sqrt{\dfrac{1}{3}}\, xy^2$

(f) $\dfrac{xy}{x - a} - \dfrac{by}{y - b}$

2. Represent each of the rational expressions in problem 1 as the quotient of two polynomials.

3. Does the set of polynomials in one variable over I form a ring? If so, does this ring have an identity for multiplication? Does the set of rational expressions in one variable over I form a field? Does the set of polynomials in one variable over F form a field?

4. Use the field properties of algebraic expressions to prove the following.

(a) $\dfrac{4 - x^2}{x - 2} = -(x + 2)$

(b) $\dfrac{x - y}{4y^2 - x^2} - \dfrac{3}{x + 2y} = \dfrac{-4x + 7y}{x^2 - 4y^2}$

(c) $\dfrac{x^3 + 2}{x + 1} = x^2 - x + 1 + \dfrac{1}{x + 1}$

5. Factor each of the following polynomials, if possible, over I, over F, over R.

(a) $x^5 - 7x^4 + 12x^3$ (b) $x^3 - \frac{5}{2}x^2 + x$

(c) $y^2 - 2 + a^2 - 2ay$ (d) $a^4 + 4$

6. Describe the process of embedding the integral domain of polynomials in a field of rational expressions. (See problem 12, Section 4–3.)

7–3. SOLVING OPEN SENTENCES

Why do we bother to construct the system of algebraic expressions over R? We now see a reason for demanding that algebraic expressions satisfy the field axioms. For if we substitute real numbers for the indeterminates of an algebraic expression, then the expression represents a real number (barring division by zero and roots of negatives). Hence, observing certain restrictions, we may shift back and forth in our minds between the indeterminate meaning of variable and the usual meaning, with certainty that under both meanings the structure of the resulting system is that of a field. The power of our technique comes from the fact that we may change our emphasis in the middle of an argument, at one moment thinking about real numbers and at another moment about indeterminates. What might appear to be laxity in an argument is really our assurance that operationally the next line of the argument will be justified whether or not the variables represent numbers. This is the justification of "symbol pushing"; the power of symbol pushing comes from this freedom from specification.

The compatibility of the meanings of "variable" leads to a successful mixture of their uses in algebra. Consider the problem of solutions of sentences.

If an algebraic expression has variables that represent elements of a particular set T of real numbers, we say that the expression is an *open phrase* whose variables have domain T. As a special case we consider any numeral for an element of T to be an open phrase. From open phrases we construct open sentences.

Definition. If A and B are open phrases, then "$A = B$," "$A \neq B$," and "$A < B$" are *open sentences*. If p, q are open sentences, then "p and q," "p or q," and "if p, then q" are open sentences.

Since open phrases are symbols for numbers in a given set, an open sentence is a statement concerning equality or order of numbers in this set. For example,

$$(1) \qquad (x^2 - 2)(2x + 1) = 0, \qquad x \quad \text{in} \quad F$$

and

$$(2) \qquad 2y < 5 - x, \qquad x \quad \text{and} \quad y \quad \text{in} \quad N,$$

are open sentences, the first in one variable and the second in two. Note particularly the domains of the variables; (1) is a statement about equality of rational numbers, and (2) concerns the order of natural numbers.

[*Caution:* It is meaningless to refer to

$$2x + 3y$$

as an open phrase if x and y are indeterminates. It becomes an open phrase only when domains are specified for x and y. For the same reason,

$$2x + 3 = 5y$$

is not an open sentence unless x and y represent elements of a specified set. It is a good habit to include some indication of the domains of the variables when referring to open phrases and open sentences.]

For specific values of the variables, an open sentence becomes a statement about numbers which is either true or false but not both. If $x = -2$, then (1) is a false statement; if $x = -\frac{1}{2}$, then it is a true statement. If $x = 2$ and $y = 1$, then (2) is a true statement, whereas if $x = 1$ and $y = 2$, it is a false statement.

A number in F which x may represent to make (1) a true statement is called a *solution* of (1); the set of all solutions of (1) is called the *truth set* (or *solution set*) of (1). (A discussion of truth sets of sentences in one variable was given in Chapter 2.) Thus the truth set of (1) is $\{-\frac{1}{2}\}$. Note that if x had instead the domain R, then the truth set of (1) would be

$$\{-\tfrac{1}{2}, \ \sqrt{2}, \ -\sqrt{2}\}.$$

Before we can define the truth set of a sentence in two variables, we must agree upon an order of the variables and we must construct a set of ordered pairs of numbers. In sentence (2), for example, x is given as the first variable and y as the second. Furthermore, since x and y each has domain N, we must construct the set of *all possible ordered pairs* of numbers in N:

$$\{(1, 1), (1, 2), (1, 3), \ldots, (2, 1), (2, 2), (2, 3), \ldots, (3, 1), (3, 2), (3, 3), \ldots\}.$$

We call this set the *cartesian product* $N \times N$. Now an element in $N \times N$ (an ordered pair of natural numbers) is a *solution* of (2) if, when x represents the first number of the ordered pair and y the second, the resulting statement is true. The set of all solutions of (2) is its *truth set*. Thus the truth set of (2) is the set of pairs $\{(1, 1), (2, 1)\}$.

> **Definition.** Given a sentence in two ordered variables x and y with S the domain of x and T the domain of y, form the set $S \times T$ of all ordered pairs (s, t), the first of each pair being an element of S and the second an element of T. Then an element (s, t) of $S \times T$ is a *solution* of the sentence if, when x represents the first element and y the second, the sentence is a true statement. The set of all solutions is the *truth set* of the sentence.

In Chapter 2 we found that graphs of sets are useful devices for finding and expressing truth sets of sentences in one variable. We can extend these techniques to obtain graphs of sets of ordered pairs of numbers, where the first variable has a value corresponding to a point on a horizontal number line and the second variable to a point on a vertical number line, forming a cartesian coordinate system on the plane. Then for a given coordinate system, each ordered pair of numbers corresponds to a unique point of the plane. For example, the set $\{(1, 1), (1, 2), (2, 1), (3, 1)\}$ has the graph

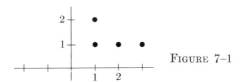

FIGURE 7-1

If each of the variables has domain R, we can also say that each point of the plane corresponds to a unique ordered pair of real numbers. Such a one-to-one correspondence between the set $R \times R$ and the set of all points of the coordinate plane is guaranteed by the completeness of R, and this fact is the basis for analytic geometry of two dimensions.

The transition from two to three ordered variables and from two to three dimensions is easy. The reader is invited to describe the set $R \times R \times R$ of all ordered triples of real numbers and to define the truth set of a sentence in three ordered variables, giving an appropriate description of the graph of such a truth set.

Before discussing solutions of sentences, we again emphasize the role of the domains of the variables. Consider the sentence

$$2y \leq 5 - x \text{ and } 2y \leq 2x + 5 \text{ and } y \geq 0,$$

where x and y have the indicated domains:

    (a) x in N and y in I,
    (b) x in I and y in N,
    (c) x in I and y in R,
    (d) x in R and y in I,
    (e) x in R and y in R.

In each case the truth set of the sentence depends on the domains of the variables. The graphs of the truth sets of the sentences are given in Fig. 7–2.

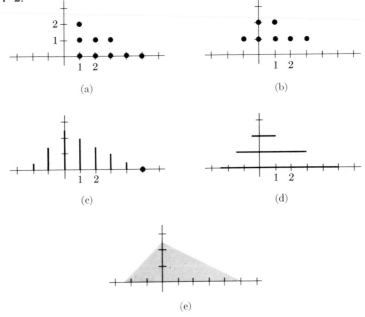

FIGURE 7–2

An example of the interplay of the algebras of real numbers and algebraic expressions is found in solving sentences in one variable. By *solving* a sentence we mean the process of determining its truth set. By a *solution* of a sentence we mean an element of its truth set. It requires little insight for a student to see that 2 is a solution of $x + 2 = 2x$, x in R. That 2 is the only solution can be shown by a simple argument: for any x greater than 2, $x + 2 < 2x$; for any x less than 2, $x + 2 > 2x$.

Hence, the truth set is $\{2\}$. But such arguments become more difficult as the sentences become more complex. Having found solutions by trial and error, how can one be sure that he has found *all* the solutions?

Consider, for example, the sentence

$$(3) \quad -3x^2 + 4x + 7x^2 - 5 - 3x = -x^2 + 5x + 4x^2 - 7,$$
$$x \text{ in } R.$$

If we regard each member of the equation as an algebraic expression, we may write formally

$$-3x^2 + 4x + 7x^2 - 5 - 3x = 4x^2 + x - 5,$$
$$-x^2 + 5x + 4x^2 - 7 = 3x^2 + 5x - 7.$$

Then (3) has the same truth set as

$$(4) \qquad 4x^2 + x - 5 = 3x^2 + 5x - 7, \qquad x \text{ in } R.$$

We are assured of this because we used certain field properties in simplifying the algebraic expressions, and these same properties hold for all real numbers. We say that two sentences are *equivalent* if they have the same truth set. Now we shift back to variables representing numbers and remark that by adding $(-3x^2 - 5x + 7)$, x in R, to both members of (4), the resulting sentence,

$$(5) \qquad x^2 - 4x + 2 = 0, \qquad x \text{ in } R,$$

is equivalent to (4). (Why is this true?) Then we factor the left member (indeterminate variable):

$$x^2 - 4x + 2 = x^2 - 4x + 4 - 2$$
$$= (x - 2)^2 - 2$$
$$= (x - 2 - \sqrt{2})(x - 2 + \sqrt{2}),$$

giving the equivalent sentence

$$(6) \quad (x - 2 - \sqrt{2})(x - 2 + \sqrt{2}) = 0, \qquad x \text{ in } R.$$

Next we use the theorem concerning real numbers (variables representing numbers):

$$\text{``}a \text{ and } b \text{ in } R, \ ab = 0 \Leftrightarrow a = 0 \text{ or } b = 0,\text{''}$$

to write the equivalent sentence

$$(7) \ x - 2 - \sqrt{2} = 0 \qquad \text{or} \qquad x - 2 + \sqrt{2} = 0, \qquad x \text{ in } R.$$

It is an easy step to the final equivalent sentence,

$$(8) \quad x = 2 + \sqrt{2} \quad \text{or} \quad x = 2 - \sqrt{2}, \quad x \text{ in } R,$$

whose truth set is, of course $\{2 + \sqrt{2}, \ 2 - \sqrt{2}\}$.

The foregoing process took us through six sentences, each equivalent to the others, until we arrived at one whose truth set is obvious. In some steps we dropped the requirement that x represent a number, and performed formal operations on algebraic expressions. In others we resumed the requirement and applied theorems concerning real numbers. In all instances we were assured of an equivalent sentence because the field properties we used hold true for all real numbers as well as for all algebraic expressions.

The preceding solution is not intended as a model to be followed. It is a typical example in which we spell out the shifting between the two meanings of "variable." It should be noted that the factorization over R leading to (6) is accomplished by the familiar "completion of the square." (A rote application of the quadratic formula at this stage obscures what is happening mathematically as well as logically.)

Not all operations on algebraic expressions lead to equivalent sentences. Note that the sentence

$$(9) \qquad \frac{x^2 - 4}{x - 2} = 4, \quad x \text{ in } R,$$

has a null truth set (no value of x in R makes this sentence true). If we shift to indeterminates and write

$$\frac{x^2 - 4}{x - 2} = x + 2,$$

the resulting sentence,

$$(10) \qquad x + 2 = 4, \quad x \text{ in } R,$$

has truth set $\{2\}$. In this case, (9) and (10) are not equivalent sentences because the formal operation, with respect to numbers in R, becomes

$$\frac{x^2 - 4}{x - 2} = x + 2 \quad \text{and} \quad x \neq 2;$$

that is, we must prohibit division by zero. Now the sentence,

$$(11) \quad x + 2 = 4 \quad \text{and} \quad x \neq 2, \quad x \text{ in } R,$$

is equivalent to (9); it also has a null truth set.

Thus formal operations on algebraic expressions lead to equivalent sentences if the results of the operations are then properly restricted to represent real numbers. We assume that when theorems on real numbers are used to obtain new sentences, the restrictions will be carefully retained.

Of course, some theorems lead to new sentences whose truth sets include those of the original sentence as proper subsets. This sometimes happens when we use the theorem:

$$\text{“}a \text{ and } b \text{ in } R,\ a = b \Rightarrow a^2 = b^2.\text{”}$$

Note that the converse of this theorem is not true. For example, the sentence,

(12) $\sqrt{2 - x} = x,\qquad x \text{ in } R,$

has its truth set included in the truth set of

(13) $2 - x = x^2,\qquad x \text{ in } R.$

The truth set of (13) is $\{-2, 1\}$, but -2 is not a solution of (12). When we apply a theorem that does not guarantee an equivalent sentence, that is, whose converse is not true, we must check individually each element of the resulting truth set in the original sentence. On the other hand, some operations may result in new sentences with smaller truth sets than were in the original sentence (such as "a and b in R, $a = b \Rightarrow a/c = b/c$," where c involves a variable). It is best to avoid this situation if, for some x, $c = 0$.

Of primary importance to a student is his understanding of the role of equivalent sentences in solving a sentence and of the types of operations and theorems resulting in equivalent sentences. Equivalence is a two-way affair. It means that every solution of the first sentence is a solution of the second, and every solution of the second is a solution of the first. If he sees how operations on algebraic expressions aid him in this procedure, he will not be tempted to treat such operations lightly.

EXERCISE GROUP 7–3

1. Solve each of the following sentences.

(a) $(x + 3)(2x - 1)(x^2 - 3) = 0,\qquad x \text{ in } I$

(b) $(x + 3)(2x - 1)(x^2 - 3) = 0,\qquad x \text{ in } F$

(c) $(x + 3)(2x - 1)(x^2 - 3) = 0,\qquad x \text{ in } R$

(d) $3x - 4 \leq x,\qquad x \text{ in } N$

(e) $3y < 6 - x,\qquad x \text{ in } N,\quad y \text{ in } N$

(f) $3y < 6 - x$ and $y \le x$, (x, y) in $N \times N$

(g) $\sqrt{x - 8} = 4 + \sqrt{x}$, x in R

(h) $x^2 \ge 4(x - 1)$, x in F

(i) $\dfrac{|x - 1|}{x - 1} = 1$ or $x > 2$, x in R

(j) $|x - 2| + 3x = 2$, x in R

2. Draw the graphs of:

(a) $x^2 - 2xy = 0$, (x, y) in $R \times R$

(b) $3x - 2 = 0$ and $y = 4x - 1$, (x, y) in $F \times F$

(c) $3y < 4x + 6$ and $y < 2$ and $2y > x$, (x, y) in $I \times R$

(d) $3y < 4x + 6$ and $y < 2$ and $2y > x$, (x, y) in $R \times R$

(e) $|x| + |y| \le 4$, (x, y) in $I \times I$

(f) $x^2 + y^2 < 4$ and $x > y$, (x, y) in $R \times R$

3. Solve (by constructing a sequence of equivalent sentences):

(a) $4 + 3x^3 - 2x + 5x^2 - x^3 = 3x + 2x^3 + 2 + 2x$, x in R

(b) $(x + 1)(x^2 - 1) = 3(x^2 - 1)$, x in R

(c) $\dfrac{1}{x} + \dfrac{1}{1 - x} + \dfrac{1}{1 + x} = 0$, x in R

(d) $\left(\dfrac{x}{x + 1}\right)(x^2 - 1) = 0$, x in R

(e) $\dfrac{x - 3}{x^2 - x - 6} = \dfrac{4}{x^2 - 4} + \dfrac{3}{2(x + 2)}$, x in R

7–4. A UNIFYING CONCEPT: FUNCTIONS

Running through our discussions of operations, correspondences, and open phrases is a common idea. We previously defined a *mapping* from a set A into a set B as a correspondence which assigns to each element of A exactly one element of B. This correspondence was also called a *function*.

There are sharp differences of opinion on the question of introducing functions at the *beginning* or at the *end* of a first course in algebra. Some current writers believe that the entire terminology of operations, variables, and expressions should be abandoned and these ideas unified at the very beginning in terms of functions. Other writers prefer to lay the groundwork for functions and then summarize the ideas by showing how functions unify the concepts studied. There seems to be no disagreement about the inclusion of functions in an intermediate or advanced algebra course. There functions should occupy a central position.

In reviewing the major ideas of elementary algebra, we recall such statements as the following.

(1) Operations

For each pair of numbers a and b in R there is a unique number $a + b$ in R.

This operation assigns to *each* element in $R \times R$ exactly *one* element in R.

Each element a in N has a unique reciprocal $1/a$ in R.

This operation assigns to *each* element of N exactly *one* element $1/a$ in R.

(2) Correspondences

There is a one-to-one correspondence between the set of even natural numbers and N.

This correspondence assigns to *each* element n in N exactly *one* element $2n$ in N and assigns to *each* element e in E (even natural numbers) exactly *one* element n in N.

(3) Algebraic expressions

$$3x^2 + x - 2y^2, \quad (x, y) \quad \text{in} \quad R \times R.$$

This algebraic expression assigns to *each* element (x, y) in $R \times R$ exactly *one* element $(3x^2 + x - 2y^2)$ in R.

(4) Variables

Let x be the number of feet in the length of a rectangle.

The variable x assigns to *each* rectangle in the set of all rectangles exactly *one* number (of feet in its length) in R.

(5) Open sentences

$$y = \sqrt{x}, \quad x \text{ in } N \quad \text{and} \quad y \text{ in } R.$$

This sentence assigns to *each* element x in N exactly *one* element y in R (for which the sentence is true).

(6) Sets of ordered pairs

$$\{(0, 2), (1, 2), (3, \pi), (4, \sqrt{2}), (5, \pi)\}.$$

This set of ordered pairs assigns to *each* element in $\{0, 1, 3, 4, 5\}$ exactly *one* element in R.

(7) Graphs of sentences

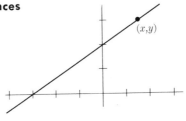

FIGURE 7–3

This graph assigns to *each* element x (abscissa) in R exactly *one* element y (ordinate) in R.

It is evident that a common concept runs through the above examples. In each of the statements (1) through (7), some rule, or operation, or association, or correspondence assigns to *each* element in a given set a *unique* element in R, resulting in a pairing-off of elements from the two sets in such a way that *no two distinct elements of the second set are assigned to the same element of the first set.* To be sure, there are correspondences which pair off elements of nonnumerical sets, such as the correspondence of each human being with a color (of his hair). In fact, wherever "of" or a possessive form of a noun is used, there is a correspondence between elements of two sets. Let us restate the definition of a mapping or function (with respect to sets of numbers).

Definition. Given a set D of numbers and a correspondence which assigns to each number in D exactly one number in R, the resulting association of numbers is called a *function*. D is called the *domain* of definition of the function, and the set of assigned numbers in R is called the *range* of the function.

Recall that a function is usually designated by a letter, such as f. The fact that f maps D into R, may be indicated in various ways:

$$f: x \to y, \qquad x \overset{f}{\to} y, \qquad f(x) = y, \qquad (x, f(x));$$
$$x \text{ in } D, \qquad y \text{ in } R.$$

The third of these notations is most commonly used in a first course in algebra. It is read "f of x is equal to y"; that is, the number assigned by the f-function to x is y. Note that $f(x)$ is not "f times x," but rather that $f(x)$ is a number. The fourth notation indicates that each x is paired with the unique number $f(x)$ assigned to x by the f-function.

A common misconception among students is that functions cannot be defined—in fact, do not exist—unless there is a formula (algebraic expression) involved in the definition. We must convince them that a function is a concept, an idea, and not a formula. There are many ways of representing a function. For example, the function described above in example (5) can be represented variously by:

A set of ordered pairs: $\{(1, 1), (2, \sqrt{2}), (3, \sqrt{3}), (4, 2), \ldots\}$.
A verbal statement: To each x in N assign the number $\sqrt{x}$ in R.
An equation: $y = \sqrt{x}$, x in N, y in R.
A formula: $f: x \to \sqrt{x}$, x in N.
A graph:

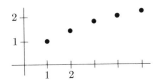

None of these representations is the function, but each describes the function. The point is that a function does not depend for its definition on its representation but only on its domain of definition and its rule of assignment. In general, two functions are *equal* if their domains are the same set and their rules of assignment are the same, regardless of the manner in which they are represented. For example, consider the two functions

$$f: \quad a \to 2a + 1, \quad a \text{ in } I,$$
$$g: \quad x \to 2x + 1, \quad x \text{ in } R.$$

These functions are different because they have different domains, even though their rules of assignment are the same.

Frequently, the rule of assignment is given for a function without mention of a specific domain of definition. In such a case the domain is understood to be the largest set of real numbers to which the rule can be applied sensibly. For example, if a function is defined as $f: x \to \sqrt{x + 2}$, then, unless otherwise stated, the domain is understood to be the set of all real numbers greater than or equal to -2.

Not all correspondences between sets of numbers define functions. This is another point of confusion for students. For example, the equation

$$y^2 = x, \quad x \text{ and } y \text{ in } R,$$

does *not* define a function $f: x \to y$ because to each element x in R this equation assigns *two* elements y and $-y$ in R. Of course, we may write

$$y^2 = x \Leftrightarrow y = \sqrt{x} \text{ or } y = -\sqrt{x}$$

and regard the equation as defining two functions. This is precisely how we would handle this equation in certain situations in the calculus. On the other hand, the equation $y^2 = x$, x and y in R, *does* define a function g, where $g(y) = y^2$.

Some functions may not be represented by formulas, but this does not disqualify them as functions. For example, the first-class postage regulations define a function: to each real number x (in ounces) in the set $\{0 < x \leq 320\}$ there is assigned a natural number y (in cents) according to the graph on the right. We could also describe this function verbally or represent it as a table of pairs of numbers, but we cannot find a single algebraic expression which represents y for a given x. Nevertheless, a function is defined.

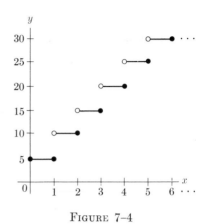

FIGURE 7-4

From this point of view, we can say that an *algebraic expression in one variable in which the variable represents a number defines a function*.

The *graph* of a function f is the graph of the truth set of the sentence $y = f(x)$, with x in the domain of f. Thus, if a is in the domain of f, then $\big(a, f(a)\big)$ is a point on the graph of f. From the definition of a function, we see that there cannot be two points on the graph of f with the same abscissa and distinct ordinates. This is the same as saying that if a vertical line is drawn through the graph of f, it will intersect the graph in exactly one point. Thus, the graph in Fig. 7–5(a) describes a function, whereas the graph in Fig. 7–5(b) does not.

For a student the graphical representation of a function is probably more informative than any other method. For instance, Fig. 7–5(a) shows the graph of the absolute-value function defined by the equation $f(x) = |x|$. From the graph it is easy to see that another representation is given by

$$f(x) = \begin{cases} x, & \text{if } x \geq 0, \\ -x, & \text{if } x < 0, \end{cases}$$

which is a statement of the definition of $|x|$.

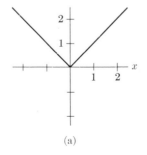

(a)

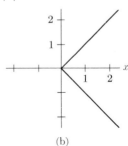

(b)

FIGURE 7-5

The study of linear and quadratic functions is aided by graphs, and the subtleties of domains of definition are often cleared up by graphical representation.

A final word to teachers: When students are introduced to functions, the introduction must be clear and precise. Too often we still read or hear, "If y depends on x for its value, then y is a function of x." Such a statement is meaningless, at best. It would be better to omit all mention of functions than to present a confused meaning of them. But if a student really understands functions, he can begin to see a unity and coherence in the variety of topics he studied in algebra.

EXERCISE GROUP 7–4

1. Each of the following is a representation of a function; give three other representations and describe the function's domain and range.

(a) To each positive integer n there is assigned its remainder after division of n by 5.

(b)

(c) $\{(1, 5), (2, 8), (3, 11), (4, 14), (5, 17), \ldots\}$

(d) $f(x) = |x + 2|$, x in $\{-3, -2, 1, 2\}$.

2. Determine the largest possible domain of each of the functions defined as follows.

(a) $f(x) = \dfrac{1}{x} - x^2$

(b) $g(x) = \sqrt{x^2 - 4}$

(c) $h(x) = \sqrt{\dfrac{x}{x - 1}}$

(d) $k(x) = \sqrt{|x + 1|}$

3. How are the functions in each of the following pairs related?

(a) $f(x) = x - 2$,

$F(t) = \dfrac{t^2 - 4}{t + 2}$

(b) $g(x) = x^2 - 1$,

$G(t) = \dfrac{t^4 - 1}{t^2 + 1}$

(c) $h(x) = \sqrt{(x - 1)^2}$,

$H(t) = |t - 1|$

4. Consider the function f defined by the rule

$$f(x) = \begin{cases} -1, & \text{if } -1 \leq x < 0 \\ x, & \text{if } 0 < x \leq 2 \end{cases}$$

(a) What numbers are represented by $f(-\frac{1}{2})$, $f(\sqrt{5})$, $f(\frac{3}{2})$?
(b) What is the domain of f?
(c) What is the range of f?
(d) What is the truth set of the equation $f(x) = x$?
(e) Draw the graph of the truth set of the sentence $f(x) < 1$.

5. Given the function g defined by

$$g(x) = x^2 - 1, \qquad x \text{ in } R.$$

If t is in R, what numbers are represented by

$$g(-t), \qquad -g(t), \qquad 2g(t), \qquad g(2t), \qquad g(t-1), \qquad g(t)-1,$$

$$g\big(g(t)\big), \qquad g\left(g\left(\frac{1}{t}\right)\right), \qquad g\left(\frac{1}{g(t)}\right)?$$

6. Draw the graph of a function f which satisfies the conditions

$$f(-1) = -2, \qquad f(0) = f(1) = 0, \qquad f(2) = 2,$$
$$f(x) < 0 \quad \text{for} \quad -1 < x < 0,$$
$$\text{and} \quad f(x) > 0 \quad \text{for} \quad 0 < x < 1 \quad \text{and for} \quad 1 < x < 2.$$

Is there only one function satisfying these conditions?

7. Which of the following graphs define functions?

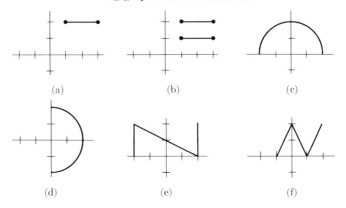

(a)   (b)   (c)

(d)   (e)   (f)

8. If a function f is defined by the graph

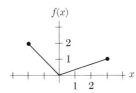

draw the graphs of the following functions:

(a) g, where $g(x) = -f(x)$, $-2 \leq x \leq 3$
(b) h, where $h(x) = f(-x)$, $-3 \leq x \leq 2$
(c) k, where $k(x) = f(x) + 2$, $-2 \leq x \leq 3$
(d) t, where $t(x) = f(x+2)$, $-4 \leq x \leq 1$.

9. If the functions f and g are defined by

$$f(x) = 2x + 1, \quad x \text{ in } R; \quad g(x) = x + 2, \quad x \text{ in } R,$$

consider the function $f{\circ}g$, the *composition* of f and g, defined by

$$f{\circ}g \ (x) = f[g(x)], \quad x \text{ in } R.$$

Determine the values of:

  (a) $f{\circ}g$ (2)
  (b) $g{\circ}f$ (2)
  (c) Give two other representations of $f{\circ}g$
  (d) of $g{\circ}f$

10. Consider the functions f and g, each with domain D, and define the functions $f + g, f \cdot g$ by:

$$(f + g)(x) = f(x) + g(x), \quad x \text{ in } D;$$
$$(f \cdot g)(x) = f(x)g(x), \quad x \text{ in } D.$$

If

$$f(x) = x^2 + 1 \quad \text{and} \quad g(x) = \frac{1}{x^2 + 1}, \quad x \text{ in } R,$$

determine:

  (a) $(f + g)(1)$ (b) $(g + f)(1)$
  (c) $(f \cdot g)(\sqrt{2})$ (d) $(g \cdot f)(\sqrt{2})$

11. Consider the set A of all first-degree polynomial functions with domain R and the binary operation $\circ$ of composition of functions. Is the system $(A, \circ)$ a group? If so, what is the identity for $\circ$? If f is defined by $f(x) = ax + b$, $a \neq 0$, does f have an inverse for all a and b? Is $\circ$ commutative?

12. Consider the set B of all polynomial functions with domain R and the binary operations $+$ and $\cdot$. Is the system $(B, +)$ a group? If so, what is an identity for $+$? What is the inverse of the element f under $+$? Is $(B, +, \cdot)$ a ring? a ring with an identity? a commutative ring? a regular ring? a field?

Chapter 8

The Complex Number System

8-1. COMPLEX NUMBERS

There are some desirable properties that the set R of real numbers does not have. For one, the equation $x^2 + 1 = 0$ does not have a solution in R. As long ago as the beginning of the nineteenth century attempts were made to develop a number system in which such equations would have solutions. In the 1840's Hamilton defined the *complex number system* as follows. He associated each point of the plane with a *complex number* denoted by an ordered pair of real numbers (a, b), just as each point of the number line is associated with a real number. His initial problem was to define equality, addition, and multiplication of these "points" in such a way that the resulting system of complex numbers is a *field* which includes the system of real numbers as a proper subsystem. He was motivated in his definitions by the desire to have the solutions of the equation $x^2 = -1$ in this system and by the observation that complex numbers should add as vectors (Fig. 8-1).

Definition. Consider the set Z of all ordered pairs (a, b), a and b in R, with "$=$," "$+$," "$\cdot$" defined for these elements as follows: for a, b, c, d, in R, (a, b) and (c, d) are in Z and

$(a, b) = (c, d) \Leftrightarrow a = c$ and $b = d$,

$(a, b) + (c, d) = (a + c, b + d)$,

$(a, b) \cdot (c, d) = (ac - bd, ad + bc)$.

The resulting system $(Z, +, \cdot)$ is called the *complex number system*.

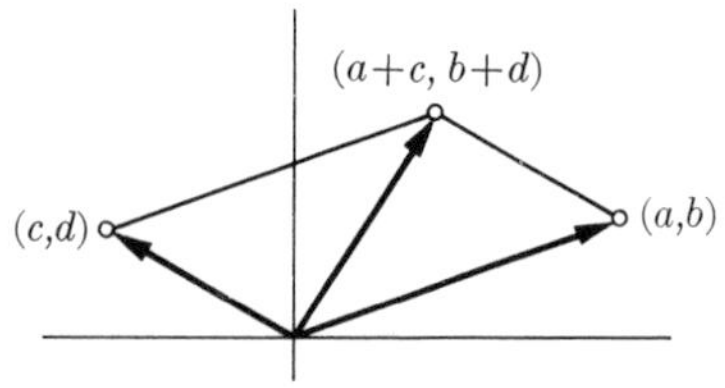

Figure 8-1

The reader is invited to use the properties of operations in R to prove that $=$ is an equivalence, the set Z is closed under the operations $+$, $\cdot$ as defined above, that these operations are commutative and associative, and that is distributive through $+$. Since

$$(a, b) + (0, 0) = (a, b) \quad \text{and} \quad (a, b) \cdot (1, 0) = (a, b)$$

for all a, b in R, the system contains an additive identity $(0, 0)$ and a multiplicative identity $(1, 0)$. Also, since

$$(a, b) + (-a, -b) = (0, 0) \qquad \text{for all} \quad a, b \quad \text{in} \quad R,$$

and

$$(a, b) \cdot \left(\frac{a}{a^2 + b^2}, \frac{-b}{a^2 + b^2} \right) = (1, 0) \qquad \text{for all} \quad (a, b) \neq (0, 0),$$

the system contains an additive inverse

$$(-a, -b)$$

for each element (a, b) and a multiplicative inverse

$$\left(\frac{a}{a^2 + b^2}, \frac{-b}{a^2 + b^2} \right)$$

for each nonzero element (a, b). We conclude that the system $(Z, +, \cdot)$ satisfies axioms F1 through F7 and is a field; all the properties proved for a field are shared by the system of complex numbers.

It should be noted immediately that the particular subset R' of Z consisting of all complex numbers of the form $(a, 0)$ is a very familiar set. Consider the following properties:

$$(a, 0) = (c, 0) \Leftrightarrow a = c \qquad \text{for} \quad a, c \text{ in } R,$$

$$(a, 0) + (c, 0) = (a + c, 0) \qquad \text{for} \quad a, c \text{ in } R,$$

$$(a, 0) \cdot (c, 0) = (ac, 0) \qquad \text{for} \quad a, c \text{ in } R,$$

$$(a, 0) + (-a, 0) = (0, 0) \qquad \text{for all } a \text{ in } R,$$

$$(a, 0) \cdot (\tfrac{1}{a}, 0) = (1, 0) \qquad \text{for all } a \neq 0 \text{ in } R.$$

We conclude that the system $(R', +, \cdot)$ is also a field. In fact, it is in every respect identical with the field of real numbers. If we define a mapping f of R' onto R so that f pairs $(a, 0)$ with a, we see that f is a one-to-one mapping that pairs sums and products in R' with sums and products of corresponding elements in R:

$$(a, 0) \leftrightarrow a \text{ and } (c, 0) \leftrightarrow c \Rightarrow \begin{cases} (a, 0) + (c, 0) \leftrightarrow a + c, \\ (a, 0) \cdot (c, 0) \leftrightarrow ac. \end{cases}$$

It should be recalled that such an operation preserving one-to-one onto mapping is called an isomorphism. Two systems are isomorphic if there is an isomorphism between them. In this case we say that the systems have the same structure. Hence we adopt the convention that R' and R are the same system, and we write a in place of $(a, 0)$ whenever convenient. In this sense we have shown that the set R is a subset of Z.

Is R a *proper* subset of Z? To answer this question in the affirmative, let us concentrate on the element $(0, 1)$ in Z. By definition,

$$(0, 1) \cdot (0, 1) = (0 - 1, 0 + 0) = (-1, 0) = -1.$$

Hence we have found an element in Z whose "square" is the real number -1. But we know that there is no real number whose square is -1 since by Theorem 3–27 the square of a real number is nonnegative; we conclude that $(0, 1)$ cannot be identified with a real number. Thus $R \neq Z$.

This complex number $(0, 1)$ is called the *imaginary unit* and is denoted by i. Now we observe that

$$(a, b) = (a, 0) + (0, b) \qquad \text{and} \qquad (0, 1) \cdot (b, 0) = (0, b)$$

implies

$$(a, b) = (a, 0) + (0, 1) \cdot (b, 0) = a + ib.$$

The notation $a + ib$ for a complex number is more convenient than (a, b) because it gives us a device for remembering the definitions of addition and multiplication of complex numbers. Making use of the associative, commutative, and distributive properties, we have

$$(a + ib) + (c + id) = (a + c) + i(b + d),$$
$$(a + ib) \cdot (c + id) = (ac + i^2 bd) + i(ad + bc)$$
$$= (ac - bd) + i(ad + bc),$$

since we have shown that $i^2 = -1$. Furthermore, $i^3 = -i$, $i^4 = 1$, $i^5 = i$, $i^6 = -1$, . . . , so that every number of the form

$$a_0 + a_1 i + a_2 i^2 + \cdots + a_n i^n,$$

where a_k is in R for each $k = 0, 1, 2, 3, \ldots, n$, can be expressed in the form $a + ib$, a and b in R.

The set of complex numbers of the form (a, b), $b \neq 0$, is called the set of *imaginary numbers*. Thus, the set Z can be considered as the enlarged set obtained by annexing to the real numbers [complex numbers of the form $(a, 0)$] the set of imaginary numbers [complex numbers of the form (a, b), $b \neq 0$].

The set Z is associated with the set of points in a plane by the simple device of referring to a pair of rectangular coordinate axes and letting each complex number (a, b) correspond to the point (a, b) in the plane, a and b in R (Fig. 8–2). Thus the real numbers correspond to the points on the horizontal (real) axis, and the imaginary numbers correspond to the points of the plane *not* on the horizontal axis. It is clear that the completeness of R guarantees that every point of the real axis corresponds to a number of the form $(a, 0)$, that every point of the vertical (imaginary) axis corresponds to a number of the form $(0, b)$, and, finally, that every point of the plane corresponds to a number of the form (a, b). All these correspondences are one-to-one.

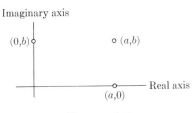

FIGURE 8-2

Let us review the properties of Z:

(1) **Closure.** The set Z is closed under addition, subtraction, multiplication, and division [excluding division by $(0, 0)$]. Of prime importance is the fact that if z is a complex number, then $\sqrt[n]{z}$ is also a complex number for any n in N. We leave this for the exercises; the proof involves a different representation of complex numbers. The equation $x^2 = a$, a in Z, has a solution in Z and, more generally, *every polynomial equation in one variable,*

$$a_n x^n + a_{n-1} x^{n-1} + \cdots + a_1 x + a_0 = 0,$$

a_i in Z, $n \geq 1$ and $a_n \neq 0$, *has a solution in Z.* This remarkable theorem, called the *fundamental theorem of algebra,* was first proved by Gauss in 1799. Thus no more extensions beyond the complex number system are necessary for solutions of polynomial equations. A consequence of the fundamental theorem is that every polynomial can be factored over Z. For example,

$$x^2 + 9 = (x + 3i)(x - 3i),$$
$$x^2 + 2x + 5 = (x + 1)^2 + 4 = (x + 1 + 2i)(x + 1 - 2i).$$

(2) **Completeness.** The system of complex numbers is complete only in the sense that there is a one-to-one correspondence between Z and the set of all points in the plane. The axiom of completeness applies only to ordered systems, and there is no way to define order for complex numbers so that the order axioms O1 through O4 hold true.

In Chapter 1 we remarked that the most important discoveries in algebra have been made in the course of studying structures of systems without regard for the models suggested. For example, a large part of modern abstract algebra was motivated by Hamilton and Cayley in the 1840's, when they looked at some known results of algebra from the point of view of structure. Their work contained some of the first illustrations of the possibility of making significant new discoveries in mathematics as a result of examining the structure of known results.

The known results at that time were the properties of real numbers. It was known that real numbers can be associated with points of a line, and that there is an ordering of the real numbers. If the real number a is positive $(a > 0)$ or negative $(a < 0)$, then $a^2 > 0$. Thus,

$$a_1^2 + a_2^2 + \cdots + a_n^2 = 0$$

implies that

$$a_1 = a_2 = \cdots = a_n = 0,$$

and

$$x^2 = b, \quad b < 0,$$

has no solution among the real numbers. Cauchy, Gauss and others* introduced a solution i of the equation $x^2 = -1$ and, adding this "imaginary" number to the real numbers, saw that the resulting number system contains all expressions of the form

$$a + bi + ci^2 + di^3 + \cdots,$$

all of which simplify to $r + si$, where $a, b, c, d, \ldots, r, s$ are real numbers. Moreover,

$$(a + bi) + (c + di) = (a + c) + (b + d)i,$$

and

$$(a + bi)(c + di) = (ac - bd) + (ad + bc)i.$$

This was the situation when Hamilton came on the scene in 1843. First of all he looked at complex numbers, as numbers of the form $a + bi$ were called, from the viewpoint of analytic geometry. Just as a point on the line corresponds to a single real number, so a point in the plane can be made to correspond to a single pair of real numbers (a, b). Thus Hamilton thought of each point of the plane as a single complex number which he denoted by a number couple (a, b). His problem was: Can multiplication of points be defined in such a way that the system has the same structure as the real numbers?

Hamilton proceeded to define addition and multiplication of points of the plane, as was done earlier in this section, and then was able to show that the resulting system, like the real numbers, has the properties of a field and also contains a solution of the equation $x^2 = -(1, 0)$, namely $x = (0, 1)$.

---

* See E. T. Bell, *Men of Mathematics*, pp. 232–234. New York: Simon and Schuster, 1937.

He observed more. The distance from the origin to the point (a, b) is given by $\sqrt{a^2 + b^2}$; if z is the complex number (a, b), we write $|z| = \sqrt{a^2 + b^2}$ and call $|z|$ the *modulus* of z. Now every complex number $z = (a, b)$ and its *conjugate* $\bar{z} = (a, -b)$ satisfy the quadratic equation with real coefficients,

$$z^2 - 2az + a^2 + b^2 = 0.$$

Also,

$$z\,\bar{z} = |z|^2 = a^2 + b^2,$$

and

$$|z_1|^2|z_2|^2 = |z_1 z_2|^2.$$

Finally, if $z_1 = (a, b)$ and $z_2 = (c, d)$, then

$$(a^2 + b^2)(c^2 + d^2) = (ac - bd)^2 + (ad + bc)^2;$$

that is, the product of two sums of two squares can be written as the sum of two squares. This result led Hamilton, Grassmann, and others to ask, Can the product of two sums of n squares be written as a sum of n squares? In other words, for what values of n can we write

$$(a_1^2 + a_2^2 + \cdots + a_n^2)(b_1^2 + b_2^2 + \cdots + b_n^2) = A_1^2 + \cdots + A_n^2,$$

where $A_1, A_2, \ldots, A_n$ are certain sums and products of $a_1, a_2, \ldots, a_n$ and $b_1, b_2, \ldots, b_n$? Here we have the second of two important problems.

The first problem can be generalized as follows. Call n-dimensional space the collection of all points $(x_1, x_2, \ldots, x_n)$, where each x_i is a real number, and add points according to the law

$$(a_1, a_2, \ldots, a_n) + (b_1, b_2, \ldots, b_n) = (a_1 + b_1, \ldots, a_n + b_n).$$

For what values of n is it possible to define multiplication of points

$$(a_1, a_2, \ldots, a_n)(b_1, b_2, \ldots, b_n) = (c_1, c_2, \ldots, c_n)$$

in such a way that the resulting system has the structure of a field?

Both problems had already been solved for $n = 2$. Hamilton made the discovery that when $n = 4$, the first problem of defining multiplication of points in 4-space is possible and the resulting system, which he called *quaternions*, had all the properties of a field except for the *commutative property* of multiplication. In the process he also solved the second problem for $n = 4$.

In 1845 Cayley showed that both problems have a solution for $n = 8$; however, in this case neither the commutative nor the associative properties of multiplication hold.

Much effort was subsequently expended on both problems. In 1898 Hurwitz proved that the second problem has a solution only for $n = 1, 2,$ 4, 8. The other problem remained unsolved until 1940 when the Swiss mathematician Hopf used powerful new methods of algebraic topology to show that the first problem has solutions only for n a power of 2. Then in 1957, using still more refined topological methods, M. Kervaire and J. Milnor, independently, gave a solution.

The result is that Hamilton and Cayley had found them all: the only values of n for which we can successfully define multiplication of points in n-space are 1, 2, 4, 8.

EXERCISE GROUP 8–1

1. Using the definition of operations on complex numbers, prove that in the system $(Z, +, \cdot)$:

(a) multiplication is associative
(b) multiplication is distributive through addition
(If $u = (a, b)$, $v = (c, d)$, $w = (e, f)$, then $u(v + w) = uv + uw$.)

2. Using the definition of equality of complex numbers, prove that:

(a) $(a, b) = (c, d)$ and $(c, d) = (e, f) \Rightarrow (a, b) = (e, f)$
(b) $(a, b) = (c, d) \Rightarrow (a, b) + (e, f) = (c, d) + (e, f)$
(c) $(a, b) = (c, d) \Rightarrow (a, b) \cdot (e, f) = (c, d) \cdot (e, f)$

3. Solve for x in Z:

(a) $x^2 + 4 = 0$ (b) $x^2 + x + 1 = 0$
(c) $2x^3 - 4x^2 = 3x$ (d) $(x - 3)(x^2 - 5)(x^2 + 9) = 0$

4. If $u = (3, -1)$, $v = (-4, 2)$, $w = (0, 3)$, compute

(a) $u + v$ (b) $\dfrac{v}{w}$

(c) $u(v + w)$ (d) $v - \dfrac{w}{u}$

(e) $\bar{u}u$ (f) $\overline{uv} - \bar{u}w$
(g) $u^2 - v^2$ (h) $\overline{uv}\,w$

5. We associated with each element $z = (a, b)$ in Z a number $|z| = \sqrt{a^2 + b^2}$ in R, called the *modulus* of z, which represents the distance between the points $(0, 0)$ and (a, b). Show that if u and v are in Z, then:

(a) $|u| \cdot |v| = |u \cdot v|$
(b) $|u + v| \le |u| + |v|$
(c) $|u|^2 = u \cdot \bar{u}$
(d) If we establish an order $\prec$ among elements of Z by the definition

$$u \prec v \Leftrightarrow |u| < |v|,$$

which, if any, of the order axioms are satisfied?

In problems 6 through 9 we lead up to the proof that Z is closed under the operation of extracting a root; that is, if z is in Z and n is in N, then the equation $x^n = z$ has a solution in Z. (Note that we cannot speak of the principal, or positive, nth root of z unless z is a positive real number.) Moreover, we shall show that the equation $x^n = z$ has exactly n solutions in Z. We assume that the reader knows some facts about trigonometric functions.

6. If $z = (a, b)$ is an element of Z (a and b in R), then consider the angles θ such that $\tan \theta = b/a$. The quadrant in which θ lies depends in a natural way on the signs of b and a. Show that

$$a = |z| \cos \theta \quad \text{and} \quad b = |z| \sin \theta,$$

so that

$$(a, b) = (|z| \cos \theta, |z| \sin \theta).$$

(It is helpful to identify (a, b) with a point of the plane and interpret θ and $|z|$ accordingly.) Hence infer that

$$a + ib = |z|(\cos \theta + i \sin \theta).$$

7. Prove by finite induction that for any n in N,

$$z^n = (a + ib)^n = |z|^n(\cos n\theta + i \sin n\theta).$$

[*Hint:* Recall the identities for $\sin (\alpha + \beta)$ and $\cos (\alpha + \beta)$.] This result is know as De Moivre's Theorem.

8. Given any z in Z show that we may write

$$z = a + ib = |z| \left(\cos (\theta_0 + 2\pi k) + i \sin (\theta_0 + 2\pi k) \right),$$

where $0 \leq \theta_0 \leq 2\pi$ and k is any integer.

9. Show that if there is a solution x of the equation $x^n = z$, we may write the equation in the form

$$|x|^n(\cos n\phi + i \sin n\phi) = |z| \left(\cos (\theta_0 + 2\pi k) + i \sin (\theta_0 + 2\pi k) \right)$$

for some angle ϕ. Solve this equation for x and ϕ, recalling the definition of equality for complex numbers. Verify that there are exactly n values of ϕ. Then show that

$$x = |x|(\cos \phi + i \sin \phi)$$

is a solution for each value of ϕ.

10. Solve for x in Z.

(a) $x^4 = -1$
(c) $x^2 = 2(1 - i\sqrt{3})$

(b) $x^3 = i$
(d) $x^6 = -64$.

8–2. ALGEBRAIC NUMBERS

When a student visualizes the set Z of complex numbers, he usually thinks of two subsystems, the reals and the imaginaries, which are *disjoint*. That is, a complex number is either real or imaginary, but not both. When he visualizes the set R of real numbers, he usually thinks of two subsystems, the rationals and the irrationals, also disjoint. Most students are content to let the matter rest there.

The mathematician, however, is forever classifying. He knows that the set of rationals is countable and the set of irrationals is not. The following questions naturally come to his mind: (1) Are there other possible classifications of the complex numbers and of the reals? (2) Is the set F of rationals the largest countable subset of R? His curiosity leads him to the discovery that there *are* other classifications, and that there *is* a countable subset of R which contains F as a proper subset.

The second of these results usually surprises a student. Why should he be surprised? Possibly because he has had a limited experience with irrationals. When asked for an example of an irrational, he will probably say, "$\sqrt{2}$" or "$\sqrt[n]{x}$," where x is an integer which is not a perfect nth power." When asked for an example of an irrational which is not obtained as a root, he will seldom respond with π. Even if he has studied logarithms and trigonometry, he is not likely to give $\log 2$ or $\sin 2$ as an example. Somehow he thinks of the values of logarithmic and trigonometric functions as "different" numbers which are real but vaguely unrelated to the properties of the reals. To him the bulk of the irrationals is found among the nth roots of integers. We shall show that this is not the case.

How can we characterize numbers which are obtained as roots? By definition, $\sqrt[5]{3}$ is a solution of the polynomial equation $x^5 - 3 = 0$; $1 + \sqrt{2}$ is a solution of the polynomial equation $x^2 - 2x - 1 = 0$, as the reader may verify. These and other examples suggest a new classification of the real numbers in terms of solutions of certain polynomial equations. In the following, we use the word "polynomials" to mean polynomials with integers for coefficients.

Definition. The number x is called *algebraic* if it is a solution of some polynomial equation

$$a_n x^n + a_{n-1} x^{n-1} + \cdots + a_1 x + a_0 = 0,$$

where each a_i is in I and n is in N. If x is not algebraic, it is called *transcendental*.

Let us restrict our attention for the moment to the real numbers. A real number is either algebraic or transcendental, but not both, depending on whether or not it is a solution of some polynomial equation.

What is to be learned from such a new classification? First, we note that all rational numbers are algebraic (being solutions of $ax - b = 0$, a and b in I, $a \neq 0$) and all real numbers of the form $\sqrt[n]{a}$, a in I, $a \geq 0$, are algebraic. But some real numbers of the form $\sqrt[n]{a}$ are not rational. Thus, the set of real algebraic numbers includes F as a *proper* subset. But is the set of real algebraic numbers countable?

The answer is "yes." We arrive at this result as follows: First, let us accept without proof the fact that corresponding to each algebraic number A there is a polynomial equation of lowest degree n such that A is a solution of the equation. For instance, if A is the rational number p/q, there is an equation of first degree, namely $qx - p = 0$, which is satisfied by A. If $A = \sqrt[n]{a}$, there is an nth-degree equation, $x^n - a = 0$, which is satisfied by A. In general, we would follow the line of reasoning used in the following example.

Consider the algebraic number

$$x = \frac{-13 + \sqrt{115}}{2}.$$

Then

$$2x + 13 = \sqrt{115}, \quad \text{and} \quad 4x^2 + 52x + 169 = 115;$$

thus

$$2x^2 + 26x + 27 = 0$$

is a polynomial equation of lowest degree, namely 2, whose solution is

$$\frac{-13 + \sqrt{115}}{2}.$$

We see that this is the lowest degree because we must square both members of the equation to obtain a polynomial equation.

Next, we define the *index* of the polynomial equation

$$a_n x^n + a_{n-1} x^{n-1} + \cdots + a_1 x + a_0 = 0$$

to be the positive integer

$$h = n + |a_n| + |a_{n-1}| + \cdots + |a_1| + |a_0|.$$

Now for each positive integer h there is a finite number of polynomial equations having index h. For example, there are exactly two equations with index $h = 2$, namely, $x = 0$ and $-x = 0$. There are eight equations with index 3:

$$2x = 0, \quad -2x = 0, \quad x + 1 = 0, \quad x - 1 = 0,$$
$$-x - 1 = 0, \quad -x + 1 = 0, \quad x^2 = 0, \quad -x^2 = 0.$$

There are 22 equations with index 4:

$$x + 2 = 0, \qquad x - 2 = 0, \qquad -x - 2 = 0, \qquad -x + 2 = 0,$$
$$2x + 1 = 0, \qquad 2x - 1 = 0, \qquad -2x - 1 = 0, \qquad -2x + 1 = 0,$$
$$3x = 0, \qquad -3x = 0, \qquad x^2 + x = 0, \qquad x^2 - x = 0,$$
$$-x^2 - x = 0, \qquad -x^2 + x = 0, \qquad x^2 + 1 = 0, \qquad x^2 - 1 = 0,$$
$$-x^2 - 1 = 0, \qquad -x^2 + 1 = 0, \qquad 2x^2 = 0, \qquad -2x^2 = 0,$$
$$x^3 = 0, \qquad -x^3 = 0.$$

(Note that we are considering only real numbers and thus will discard the equations $x^2 + 1 = 0$ and $-x^2 - 1 = 0$.)

How many polynomial equations have index 5?

Now we have a scheme for counting the algebraic numbers. For each successive value of $h = 2, 3, 4, 5, \ldots$, there is a finite number of polynomial equations with index h, each with a finite number of roots that can be listed in some order. Thus, there is a one-to-one correspondence between N and the set of algebraic numbers. As a consequence, the set of algebraic numbers is countable and has F as a proper subset.

What are some properties of the real algebraic numbers? It can be shown that they satisfy the axioms for an ordered field but *not* the completeness axiom. Also, since the set of real algebraic numbers is countable, the set of real transcendental numbers is *not* countable. (Otherwise, if both the algebraic and transcendental numbers were countable, then R would be countable, contrary to fact.) Thus we see that the bulk of the irrationals is found among the real transcendental numbers.

Here we have a strange situation. There are "more" transcendental numbers than algebraic numbers, but in our study we have not proved the existence of even a single transcendental number. In fact, such a proof is extremely difficult and was not accomplished until the late nineteenth century.

The most familiar transcendental real numbers are π and e. It was not known until the nineteenth century that π is irrational, and not until 1882, when the proof was given by the German mathematician, Lindeman, that it is also transcendental. It is fascinating to follow the history of the growing understanding of π, the ratio of the circumference of a circle to its diameter. The Bible approximates π as 3; school children approximate it as $\frac{22}{7}$. For centuries it was assumed rational, and a favorite unsolved problem was that of "squaring" the circle—finding with ruler and compass a square whose area is that of a given circle. Since operations with straightedge and compass are analogous to solutions of first- and second-degree polynomial equations, we now know that the circle cannot be "squared" because π is transcendental and, hence, cannot be the root of such an equation.

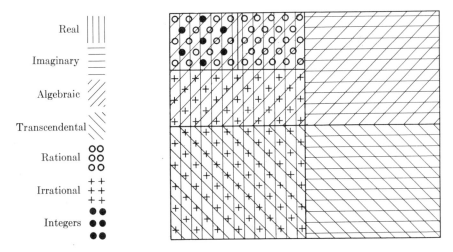

FIGURE 8–3

The number e, which is the lub of the set

$$\left\{\left(1 + \frac{1}{1}\right)^1, \left(1 + \frac{1}{2}\right)^2, \ldots, \left(1 + \frac{1}{n}\right)^n, \ldots\right\},$$

is represented by 2.7182818...; it was encountered in the development of logarithms and is used as the "natural" base of logarithms. In 1873 the Frenchman, Hermite, proved that e is transcendental. The transcendence of real numbers such as $2^{\sqrt{2}}$ and log 2 are more recent results,* known only since 1934, when it was proved that α^β is transcendental if α is algebraic, α different from 0 or 1, and β is algebraic and irrational. This result establishes the transcendence of log r if r is rational and log r is irrational: by definition, $10^{\log r} = r$. Now if log r were algebraic and irrational, then r would be transcendental, according to the above theorem. But r is given as rational; hence, log r is transcendental.

To summarize, we diagram the complex number system as shown in Fig. 8–3. [The relative areas of the regions in the above diagram do not in any way indicate the relative sizes (cardinalities) of the various sets.]

Thus we see that every complex number is either algebraic or transcendental, but not both. Every real transcendental number is irrational, but some irrational numbers are algebraic; and every rational number is algebraic, but some algebraic numbers are irrational.

---

* See Chapter 5 of the SMSG Monograph, *Numbers: Rational and Irrational*, by Ivan Niven, Random House, New York, 1961, for a discussion of these results. Also see Chapter 7 for a proof of the existence of a real transcendental number.

EXERCISE GROUP 8–2

1. *Prove:* If A is algebraic and T is transcendental, then

(a) $A + T$ is transcendental

(b) AT is transcendental

(c) $\sqrt[n]{T}$ is transcendental

2. If we assume that the set of algebraic numbers is closed under $+$ and $\cdot$, is the set of transcendental numbers closed under

(a) addition,   (b) multiplication,   (c) division?

3. Let Z = complex numbers, A = algebraic numbers, T = transcendental numbers, R = real numbers, G = imaginary numbers, F = rational numbers, H = irrational numbers. Give an example, if possible, of an element

(a) in A and not in T (b) in A and in T

(c) in A and not in R (d) in A and in R

(e) in A and not in G (f) in A and in G

(g) in T and in R (h) in T and not in R

(i) in T and in F (j) in T and not in F

(k) in T and in Z (l) in T and not in Z

(m) in T and in H (n) in T and not in H

References

Birkhoff, G., and S. MacLane, *A Survey of Modern Algebra*, Rev. Ed., Macmillan, New York, 1953. (A classic in the field.)

Courant, R., and H. Robbins, *What is Mathematics?*, Oxford University Press, New York, 1941.

Kamke, E., *Theory of Sets*, Dover Publications, New York, 1950.

Landau, E., *Foundations of Analysis*, Chelsea, New York, 1951. (A careful description of a construction of the real number system from the natural numbers.)

Moore, J. T., *Elements of Abstract Algebra*, Macmillan, New York, 1962. (A useful supplement, especially for Chapter 1.)

Mostow, G. D., J. H. Sampson, and J. Meyer, *Fundamental Structures of Algebra*, McGraw-Hill, New York, 1963. (Quite useful as a general reference, particularly for Chapters 1, 4, and 5.)

Northrop, E. P., and Staff, *Fundamental Mathematics*, University of Chicago Press, Chicago, 1948. (This work was probably the leader in the "new approach" to mathematics.)

Polya, G., *Mathematics of Plausible Reasoning*, Vols. I, II, Princeton University Press, 1959.

Stabler, E. R., *An Introduction to Mathematical Thought*, Addison-Wesley, Reading, Mass., 1953. (A reference for Chapter 2.)

Thurston, H. A., *The Number-System*, Interscience, New York, 1956. (Describes a development of the real number system.)

Answers

1. $E \times O = E$, $O \times E = E$; O is an identity for $\times$. $\times$ is distributive through $+$, but $+$ is *not* distributive through $\times$, since $O + (O \times E) \neq (O + O) \times (O + E)$.

2. The set is closed under $\circ$ and $*$. $\circ$ is commutative, but $*$ is not. r is an identity for $\circ$. There is no identity for $*$. $\circ$ is not distributive through $*$, and $*$ is not distributive through $\circ$. Every element has an inverse under $\circ$.

3. This set and this binary operation form an algebraic system closed under $\circ$. $\circ$ is commutative and associative. C is an identity element for $\circ$, and every element has an inverse under $\circ$. The system is a commutative group.

$\circ$	A	B	C
A	B	C	A
B	C	A	B
C	A	B	C

4. $(X, \circ)$ is not a commutative group. I is an identity for $\circ$. S_2 is an inverse of S_2. (a) S_2 (b) S_2 (c) I (d) R_1

5. Yes   6. Yes

7. This is not a group since v does not have an inverse and $++$ is not associative; for example,

$$u ++ (u ++ v) = u ++ r = u, \qquad \text{but} \qquad (u ++ u) ++ v = r ++ v = v$$

9. $(E, +, \times)$ is a ring. There is no identity for $\times$.

10. (a) Ring   (b) Ring   (c) Ring

12. $(T, \oplus, \odot)$ is a commutative ring. The inverse of 2 under $\oplus$ is 2. 2 does not have an inverse under $\odot$.

14. (a) No
    (b) Yes, with respect to addition; no, with respect to multiplication
    (c) No, $*$ is not associative
    (d) No, 2 has no inverse under $\odot$
    (e) Yes

1. $C = J$, $E = H$, $A = D$

2. C, E, G, H and J are proper subsets of W. H and E are proper subsets of G.

3. (a) A 1-1 mapping of S onto T (b) A mapping of S into T
   (c) A mapping of S into T (d) Not a mapping
   (e) A mapping of S into T (f) A mapping of S into T
   (g) Not a mapping   (h) Not a mapping

4. (a) Infinite   (b) Not infinite   (c) Infinite   (d) Infinite   (e) Finite

6. (a) Yes   (b) No   (c) Yes   (d) No   (e) No
   (f) Yes   (g) No   (h) Yes   (i) No   (j) Yes

3 is a prime but 4 is not; that is $4 = 2^2$ is the product of two numbers both greater than 1, but 3 is not and, hence, the difference in answer to (a) and (b).

   (k) No   (l) Yes   (m) Yes

7. $(T, \oplus) \cong (D, \circ)$, where $0 \leftrightarrow R_4, 1 \leftrightarrow R_1, 2 \leftrightarrow R_2, 3 \leftrightarrow R_3$
   $(D, \circ) \cong (G, \cdot)$, where $R_4 \leftrightarrow 1, R_1 \leftrightarrow i, R_2 \leftrightarrow -1, R_3 \leftrightarrow -i$
   $(I, +) \cong (E, +)$, where $0 \leftrightarrow 0, 1 \leftrightarrow 2, -1 \leftrightarrow -2, 2 \leftrightarrow 4, -2 \leftrightarrow -4, \ldots$

Section 2–2

1. (a)

A	B	A and B	A or B	not-A	if A, then B	not-A or B
T	T	T	T	F	T	T
F	T	F	T	T	T	T
T	F	F	T	F	F	F
F	F	F	F	T	T	T

(b)

A	B	A and not-B	if not-A, then B	if B, then A
T	T	F	T	T
T	F	T	T	T
F	T	F	T	F
F	F	F	F	T

(c)

A	B	if A, then B	A or B	A and B	A and not-A
T	F	F	T	F	F
		not possible			
T	T	T	T	T	F
F	F	T	F	F	F

(d)

A	B	not-$(A$ or $B)$	not-A or not-B	not-$(A$ and $B)$	not-A and not-B
T	T	F	F	F	F
F	F	T	T	T	T
T	F	F	T	T	F
F	T	F	T	T	F

(e)

A	B	C	(A or B) and C	A or (B and C)	(not-A and B) or not-C
T	T	T	T	T	F
T	T	F	F	T	T
T	F	T	T	T	F
T	F	F	F	T	T
F	F	F	F	F	T
F	F	T	F	F	F
F	T	F	F	F	T
F	T	T	T	T	T

2. (a) {1, 2, 3}   (b) The set of positive integers
   (c) $\emptyset$ = empty set   (d) The set of positive integers
   (e) The set of positive integers
   (f) The set of positive integers greater than or equal to 4. {4, 5, ...}
   (g) {1, 2, 3, 4, ...}   (h) {2}   (i) {2}
   (j) {1, 2}   (k) {1, 2, 3, ...}   (l) {1, 2, 3, ...}

3.
(a)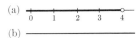

(b) ————————————————

(c) ϕ

(d) ————————————————

(e) ————————————————

(f)

(g) ————————————————

(h)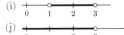

(i)

(j)

4. (a) {(1, 1), (4, 2), (9, 3), (16, 4), (25, 5), (36, 6)}   (b) {(1, 3)}
   (c) {(1, 4), (2, 3), (3, 2), (4, 1), (2, 2)}   (d) {(1, 4)}
   (e) {(1, 2), (1, 3), (1, 4), (1, 5), (2, 2), (2, 3), (2, 4), (2, 5)}
   (f) {(−1, 1), (−2, 2), (−2, 3), (−3, 2), (−3, 3)}

5.

(a)

(b)

(c)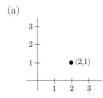

(d)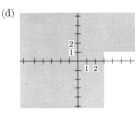

5. (*cont.*)

(e)   (f)

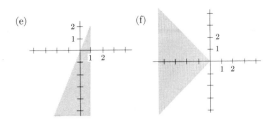

Section 2–3

1. (a)   (b)

A	B	if A, then B	not-A	not-A or B
T	T	T	F	T
F	T	T	T	T
T	F	F	F	F
F	F	T	T	T

Two statements are equivalent.

A	B	not-A	not-B	A or not-B	not-A and B
T	T	F	F	T	F
F	T	T	F	F	T
T	F	F	T	T	F
F	F	T	T	T	F

Two statements are *not* equivalent.

(c)   (d)

A	B	if A, then B	if B, then A
T	T	T	T
F	T	T	F
T	F	F	T
F	F	T	T

Two statements are *not* equivalent.

A	B	not-A	not-B	if A, then B	if not-A, then not-B
T	T	F	F	T	T
F	T	T	F	T	F
T	F	F	T	F	T
F	F	T	T	T	T

Two statements are *not* equivalent.

(e)

A	B	not-A	not-B	A and B	not-(A and B)	not-A or not-B
T	T	F	F	T	F	F
F	T	T	F	F	T	T
T	F	F	T	F	T	T
F	F	T	T	F	T	T

Two statements are equivalent.

(f)

A	B	not-A	not-B	(A or B)	not-(A or B)	not-A and not-B
T	T	F	F	T	F	F
F	T	T	F	T	F	F
T	F	F	T	T	F	F
F	F	T	T	F	T	T

Two statements are equivalent.

(g)

A	B	not-B	if A, then B	not-(if A, then B)	if A, then not-B
T	T	F	T	F	F
F	T	F	T	F	T
T	F	T	F	T	T
F	F	T	T	F	T

Two statements are *not* equivalent.

(h)

A	B	not-B	if A, then B	not-(if A, then B)	A and not B
T	T	F	T	F	F
F	T	F	T	F	F
T	F	T	F	T	T
F	F	T	T	F	F

Two statements are equivalent.

2. $A \Rightarrow B \Leftrightarrow$ not-A or B

not-$(A$ and $B) \Leftrightarrow$ not-A or not-B

not-$(A$ or $B) \Leftrightarrow$ not-A and not-B

not-$(A \Rightarrow B) \Leftrightarrow A$ and not-B

The negative of a conjunction is the disjunction of the negatives; the negative of a disjunction is the conjunction of the negatives. The negative of a conditional is a conjunction.

   (a) If not-C then (not-A and not-B)
   (b) If (not-B or not-C) then not-A
   (c) If (not-C and not-D) then (A and not-B)
   (d) If (C or D) then (not-A and B)

3. (a) Any $x < 0$ (b) Any $x \neq 0$ and $x \neq 1$
   (c) 41, 82; in fact, $41 \cdot k$ for any integer k
   (d) Any $x < 0$ (e) $x = 1$ (f) $x = 0$
   (g) $(x = 0, y = 0)$, $(x = 1, y = 1)$.   Any pair (x, x)

4. (a) Direct proof   (b) Contrapositive   (c) Proof by contradiction

Section 3–2

8. $x = (b + c) - a$ 9. $x = 1$

10. Subtraction is not commutative, $0 - 1 \neq 1 - 0$. It is not associative, since $(1 - 2) - 3 = -1 - 3 = -4$, but $1 - (2 - 3) = 1 - (-1) = 2$.

12. The set is a field with these two operations. The additive inverse of 3 is 2 and the multiplicative inverse is also 2.

13. This set is not a field, since not all nonzero elements have multiplicative inverses.

Section 3–3

8. (a) $x > \frac{3}{2}$ (b) $x \geq 1$
   (c) $1 < x < \frac{5}{3}$ (d) $x > 3$ or $x < \frac{1}{2}$
   (e) $x > -\frac{1}{2}$ or $x < -3$ (f) $x > 0$ or $x < -2$
   (g) $(x > 0$ and $x < 2)$ or $x < -2$

9. (a) $\emptyset$ (b) $x > 1$ or $x < 0$
   (c) $x < 1$ or $x > 5$ (d) $x = 0$ or $x = -2$
   (e) $1 < x < 3$ (f) All x in $\mathfrak{F}$ not equal to 2
   (g) $x > \sqrt{5}$ or $x < -\sqrt{5}$ or $-\sqrt{3} < x < \sqrt{3}$
   (h) $0 < x < 2$ (i) All x in $\mathfrak{F}$

10. (a) $\{(0, 4), (1, 3), (-1, 3), (2, 2), (-2, 2), (3, 1), (-3, 1), (4, 0), (5, -1),$
        $(6, -2), (7, -3)\}$
    (b) $\{(-3, -1), (-3, 7), (-2, -2), (-2, 6), (-1, -3), (-1, 5), (0, 4),$
        $(1, 3), (2, 2), (3, 1), (4, 0), (5, -1), (6, -2), (7, -3)\}$
    (c) $\{(-1, -3), (-1, 3), (1, -3), (1, 3), (2, 2), (-2, -2), (0, 4), (4, 0),$
        $(-3, -1), (-3, 1), (3, -1), (2, -2), (3, 1), (-2, 2), (0, -4), (-4, 0)\}$
    (d) $\emptyset$ (e) $\emptyset$ (f) $\{(1, 0), (2, 0), (3, 0), (0, 1), (1, 1), (2, 1), (3, 1)\}$

11.

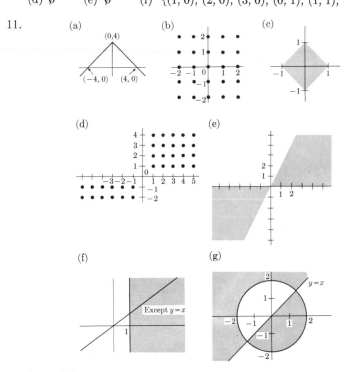

12. O1 and O2 are satisfied but O3 and O4 are not. For example, $2 < 3$ but
$2 + 2 \not< 2 + 3 = 0$; $1 < 4$ but $1 + 1 \not< 1 + 4 = 0$, and $2 < 3, 0 < 2$ but
$4 \not< 2 \cdot 3 = 1$.   13. No

17. (a) $x = 3$ (b) $x = 2$ or $x = 4$ (c) $2 < x < 4$
    (d) $\emptyset$ (e) $1 < x < 2$ (f) $-5 < x \leq 3$
    (g) $x = 1$ or $x = 3$ (h) $-3 < x < -\frac{3}{2}$

Section 4–1

2. No. There is no identity for addition; and under multiplication the system is not a group since no element of N except 1 has an inverse. $(N, +, \cdot)$ satisfies F1, F2, F3, F5, O1 through O4.

10. (a) $b = 12$, $c = 2$ (b) $b = 18$, $c = 4$ (c) $b = 15$, $c = 10$
    (d) Impossible since if $bc = 84 = 2 \cdot 2 \cdot 3 \cdot 7$ and $b + c = 24$, we have
    $3|84$ and hence $3|b$ or $3|c$. But $3|(b + c)$, and hence $3|b$ and $3|c$. But
    then $9|bc$, which is not true.

11. (a) $(x + 2)(x + 6)$ (b) $(x + 8)(x + 7)$
    (c) Cannot be factored in N (d) $(x + 18)(x + 14)$

Section 4–2

1. (a) 0 is an even integer   (b) Yes   2. (a) 90,   6,   1

3. The set of negative integers is closed under addition but not under subtraction and multiplication.

4. (a) $(932)_{\text{ten}}$ (b) $(44)_{\text{ten}}$ (c) $(110002)_{\text{three}}$ (d) $(402)_{\text{nine}}$

5. I is a group under addition but not under multiplication since 1 and -1 are the only two elements of I which have multiplicative inverses in I.

6. I is not a field because of its lack of multiplicative inverses for nonzero elements.

9. Not every composite in T can be factored uniquely into a product of primes in T. For example, 220 is in T, since $220 = 3(73) + 1$, but

$$220 = 10 \cdot 22 \quad \text{and} \quad 220 = 4 \cdot 55,$$

where 10, 22, 4, 55 are primes in T.

13. (b) $pq = 0$, $q \neq 0 \Rightarrow r(pq) = 0$ for any r in $S \Rightarrow (rp)q = 0 \Rightarrow pq = (rp)q \Rightarrow p = rp$ for any $r \Rightarrow p = 0 \cdot p = 0$

14. (a) $(E, +, \cdot)$, where E is the set of even integers
    (b) Problem 18 in Exercise Group 1–2
    (c) Problem 11 in Exercise Group 1–2
    (d) Problem 11 in Exercise Group 1–2, with a, b, c, d $even$ integers

Section 4–3

1. $-\frac{37}{61} < -\frac{12}{20} < \frac{47}{59} < \frac{4}{5}$

2. (a) $(\frac{25}{32})_{\text{ten}}$ (b) $(1.2)_{\text{four}}$ (c) $(41.1\dot{3})_{\text{five}}$ (d) $(3.043)_{\text{six}}$

7. (a) The subset of all x with $0 < x < 1$ has no least element.
   (b) Yes. 0 is the greatest element less than every element of T.

8. .$1\dot{4}2\dot{8}\dot{5}\dot{7}$

9. (a) {1}   (b) {1, −1}   (c) {1, −1, $\frac{3}{2}$}   (d) {1, −1, $\frac{3}{2}$, $\sqrt{2}$, −$\sqrt{2}$}

10. (a) $(x^2 - 3)(x^2 + 3)$ (b) $(x - \sqrt{3})(x + \sqrt{3})(x^2 + 3)$

Section 5–1

1. (a) $\frac{6}{7}$, 1 are upper bounds, for example, and $\frac{5}{7}$ is the least upper bound.

   (b) −3.5, −3, 0 or any positive number are upper bounds, and −3.6 is the lub.

3. A nonempty set S of real numbers is bounded below if there exists a real number M such that $s \geq M$ for every s in S. M is called a lower bound of S. A real number L is a greatest lower bound for S provided that (1) L is a lower bound for S and (2) if M is any lower bound for S, then $M \leq L$.

5. (a) $\frac{1}{2}$ is a lower bound and 1 is an upper bound
   (b) 0 is a lower bound and $\frac{1}{2}$ is an upper bound
   (c) 1 is a lower bound and 2 is an upper bound
   (d) 1 is a lower bound and 2 is an upper bound

6. (a) 1 is the lub   (b) 1   (c) 0   (d) 1

8. (a) lub of $T = m + 2$,   glb of $T = n + 2$
   (b) lub of $P = -2n$,   glb of $P = -2m$

9. lub of $P + S = p + s$,   lub of $P \cup S =$ maximum of p, s

Section 5–2

2. 1.414 > 1.41   but $(1.414)^2 < 2$

3. 1.415 < 1.42   but $(1.415)^2 > 2$

Section 6–2

1. (a) $\frac{41}{333}$ (b) $\frac{194}{45}$ (c) $\frac{1}{275}$ (d) $\frac{1}{7}$ (e) $\frac{635}{100}$ (f) $\frac{11}{100}$

2. (a) {1, 1.7, 1.73, 1.732}   (b) {.3, .33, .333, .3333}
   (c) {1, 1.2, 1.25, 1.259}   (d) {2, 2.2, 2.23, 2.236}

3. (a) For example, 2.3, 2.31, 2.34, . . . , 2.4 or any terminating decimal between 2.3 and 2.4
   (b) 6.6, 6.61, 6.624973, . . . , 6.63 or any terminating decimal between 6.6 and 6.63
   (c) Any terminating decimal larger than .$9\dot{3}$ and less than .$9\dot{6}$. For example, .9404, .95, .95999, .96

5. 3.1416 = $\frac{31416}{10000}$ and $\frac{22}{7}$ are rational numbers and π is not

6. (a) 1   (b) $\frac{1}{11}$two   (c) $\frac{101}{110}$two   (d) $\frac{10011}{1110}$two

Section 7–2

1. (a) Algebraic over I (b) Rational over R (c) Algebraic over I
   (d) Algebraic over I (e) Polynomial over R (f) Rational over I

2. (b) $\dfrac{\left(\dfrac{\pi}{3} - 9\right)xy - \dfrac{2\pi}{3}y + 18x}{x - 2}$ (f) $\dfrac{xy^2 - 2bxy + aby}{xy - ay - bx + ab}$

3. We know that $a - a = a + (-a) = 0$ for the real numbers, and having defined $A - A = A + (-A)$ for arbitrary algebraic expressions, we must define this to be zero in order for the field properties to be satisfied. Similarly,

$$\frac{A}{A} = A \div A = A \cdot \frac{1}{A}$$

must be 1.

4. (a) $\dfrac{4 - x^2}{x - 2} = \dfrac{(2 - x)(2 + x)}{x - 2} = \dfrac{(-1)(x - 2)\,(2 + x)}{(x - 2)}$

   $= (-1)(2 + x) \cdot \dfrac{x - 2}{x - 2} = -(x + 2)$

   (b) $\dfrac{x - y}{4y^2 - x^2} - \dfrac{3}{x + 2y} = \dfrac{x - y}{4y^2 - x^2} \cdot \dfrac{-1}{-1} - \dfrac{3}{x + 2y} \cdot \dfrac{x - 2y}{x - 2y}$

   $= \dfrac{y - x}{-4y^2 + x^2} - \dfrac{3x - 6y}{x^2 - 4y^2}$

   $= \dfrac{y - x - 3x + 6y}{x^2 - 4y^2}$

   $= \dfrac{-4x + 7y}{x^2 - 4y^2}$

   (c) $\dfrac{x^3 + 2}{x + 1} = \dfrac{x^2(x + 1) + 2 - x^2}{x + 1}$

   $= \dfrac{x^2(x + 1) + (-x)(x + 1) + (x + 1) + 1}{x + 1}$

   $= x^2 - x + 1 + \dfrac{1}{x + 1}$

5. (a) $x^3(x - 3)(x - 4)$ over I, F and R
   (b) $x(x - \frac{1}{2})(x - 2)$ over F and R
   (c) $(y + \sqrt{2} - a)\,(y - \sqrt{2} - a)$ over R
   (d) $(a^2 - 2a + 2)(a^2 + 2a + 2)$ over I, F, R

Section 7–3

1. (a) $\{-3\}$ (b) $\{-3, \frac{1}{2}\}$ (c) $\{-3, \frac{1}{2}, \sqrt{3}, -\sqrt{3}\}$
   (d) $\{1, 2\}$ (e) $\{(1, 1), (2, 1)\}$ (f) $\{(1, 1), (2, 1)\}$
   (g) The truth set is empty   (h) The truth set is F
   (i) All x in R with $x > 1$ (j) $\{0\}$

2.

(a) (b)

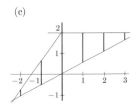

(c) (d)

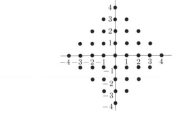

(e) (f)

3. (a) $\{1, \frac{2}{5}\}$ (b) $\{1, 2, -1\}$
   (c) $\{1 - \sqrt{2}, 1 + \sqrt{2}\}$ (d) $\{0, 1\}$
   (e) $\{-6\}$

Section 7–4

1. (a) The domain is the set of positive integers and the range is the set $\{0, 1, 2, 3, 4\}$:

   $\{(1, 1), (2, 2), (3, 3), (4, 4), (5, 0), (6, 1), (7, 2), (8, 3), (9, 4), \ldots\}$.

   As a graph

   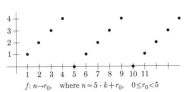

   $f: n \to r_0$, where $n = 5 \cdot k + r_0$, $0 \leq r_0 < 5$

(b) The domain is the set of all real numbers x such that $0 \leq x \leq 3$; the range is the set of real numbers y such that $0 \leq y \leq 2$.

$$f: x \to -\tfrac{2}{3}x + 2, \qquad y = -\tfrac{2}{3}x + 2$$

To each x in R between 0 and 3 there is assigned the real number y which is equal to $-\tfrac{2}{3}$ times x plus 2.

(c) The domain is the set of natural numbers and the range is the set of natural numbers of the form $3n + 2$, n a natural number: $f(n) = 3n + 2$. To each natural number n there is assigned the number obtained by adding 2 to 3 times n: f: $n \rightarrow 5 + 3(n - 1)$

(d) The domain is the set $\{-3, -2, 1, 2\}$ and the range is the set $\{1, 0, 3, 4\}$:

$$\{(-3, 1), (-2, 0), (1, 3), (2, 4)\}$$

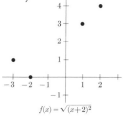

$f(x) = \sqrt{(x+2)^2}$

2. (a) All nonzero real numbers.
   (b) All real numbers less than or equal to -2 or greater than or equal to 2.
   (c) All real numbers x such that $x > 1$ or $x \leq 0$.
   (d) R

3. (a) The domain of F is contained in the domain of f and for x in the domain of F, $(x \neq -2)$, $f(x) = F(x)$.
   (b) g and G define the same function
   (c) h and H define the same function

4. (a) $f(-\frac{1}{2}) = -1$, $f(\sqrt{5})$ not defined, $f(\frac{3}{2}) = \frac{3}{2}$
   (b) The set of all x in R with $-1 \leq x < 0$ or $0 < x \leq 2$
   (c) The range of f is the set containing -1 and all real numbers less than or equal to 2 and greater than zero.
   (d) The set of all x in R with $0 < x \leq 2$ or $x = -1$
   (e)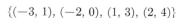

5. $g(-t) = t^2 - 1 = g(t)$
   $-g(t) = 1 - t^2$
   $2g(t) = 2(t^2 - 1)$
   $g(2t) = 4t^2 - 1$
   $g(t - 1) = t^2 - 2t$
   $g(t) - 1 = t^2 - 2$
   $g(g(t)) = t^4 - 2t^2$

   $g\left(g\left(\frac{1}{t}\right)\right) = \dfrac{1 - 2t^2}{t^4}$

   $g\left(\dfrac{1}{g(t)}\right) = \dfrac{2t^2 - t^4}{(t^2 - 1)^2}$

6. This is the graph of one function satisfying the conditions. There are infinitely many such functions.

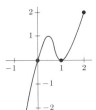

7. (a), (c), and (f) define functions

8.

(a)

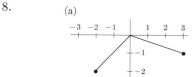

(b)

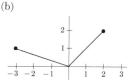

8. (*cont.*)

(c)   (d)

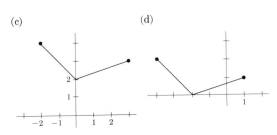

9. (a) 9   (b) 7   (c) $f{\circ}g\,(x)\,=\,2x+5$ (d) $g{\circ}f\,(x)\,=\,2x+3$

10. (a) $\frac{5}{2}$ (b) $\frac{5}{2}$

11. $(A, \circ)$ is a group. g such that $g(x)\,=\,x$ is an identity.

12. $(B, +, \cdot)$ is a commutative, regular ring with identity; it is not a field.

Section 8–1

3. (a) $\{2i,\ -2i\}$ (b) $\left\{-\dfrac{1}{2}+\dfrac{\sqrt{3}}{2}\,i,\ -\dfrac{1}{2}-\dfrac{\sqrt{3}}{2}\,i\right\}$

  (c) $\left\{0,\ 1+\dfrac{\sqrt{10}}{2},\ 1-\dfrac{\sqrt{10}}{2}\right\}$ (d) $\{3,\ \sqrt{5},\ -\sqrt{5},\ 3i,\ -3i\}$

4. (a) $(-1, 1)$ (b) $(\frac{2}{3}, \frac{4}{3})$ (c) $(-7, 19)$
   (d) $(-\frac{37}{10}, \frac{11}{10})$ (e) $(10, 0)$ (f) $(-7, -19)$
   (g) $(-4, 10)$ (h) $(6, 42)$

10. (a) $\left\{\dfrac{\sqrt{2}}{2}\,(1+i),\ \dfrac{\sqrt{2}}{2}\,(-1+i),\ \dfrac{\sqrt{2}}{2}\,(-1-i),\ \dfrac{\sqrt{2}}{2}\,(1-i)\right\}$

   (b) $\{\frac{1}{2}(\sqrt{3}+i),\ \frac{1}{2}(-\sqrt{3}+i),\ -i\}$
   (c) $\{2(-\sqrt{3}+i),\ 2(\sqrt{3}-i)\}$
   (d) $\{(\sqrt{3}+i),\ 2i,\ (-\sqrt{3}+i),\ (-\sqrt{3}-i),\ -2i,\ (\sqrt{3}-i)\}$

Section 8–2

2. The set of transcendental numbers is not closed under addition, multiplication, or division.

Index